SECOND EDITION
Water-Soluble Resins

Edited by

ROBERT L. DAVIDSON
Managing Editor-News
CHEMICAL ENGINEERING

and
MARSHALL SITTIG
Princeton University

*TP
978
.D3
1968*

REINHOLD BOOK CORPORATION
A subsidiary of Chapman-Reinhold, Inc.
New York   Amsterdam   London

Foreword

Rapid growth continues to characterize the water-soluble resins field. The development of synthetic compounds, though only a fraction of the total water-soluble resins production today, presages substantial increases in sales in the coming decade.

Water-soluble resins are used in almost every branch of industry. In 1966, total consumption of all types was more than 3 billion pounds with a value of more than $400 million. Nevertheless, until publication of the first edition of "Water-soluble Resins" in 1962, there was no adequate and comprehensive source of information on the subject.

This expanded second edition continues the objective of consolidating the current technology of water-soluble resins. Both users and producers of these materials should benefit from the broad perspective it provides.

W. Alec Jordan, President

W. ALEC JORDAN ASSOCIATES

Preface

It is difficult to name an industry that does not use a water-soluble resin. Yet prior to the first edition of "Water-soluble Resins" in 1962, little emphasis was placed on the comparative value or functionality of water-soluble polymeric materials as a class. Instead they had been classified in separate categories, usually in terms of their chemistry, sources, or end uses.

The contributing authors and the editors of "Water-soluble Resins" designed this book to be a compact and brief, but authoritative, survey of the more significant modified natural and synthetic water-soluble resins and gums available commercially. Not a scientific treatise, the book emphasizes applications, and is not limited to syntheses and physical properties. It is a book for anyone who wants to thicken a water solution, make use of water-soluble films, suspend solids, or retain moisture. The contents are designed to give an interested person sufficient information to evaluate the properties of various water-soluble resins in terms of his own needs, and to help him discuss his problems with suppliers in terms of the properties of these materials.

In presenting a broad concept of water-soluble resins as an integrated technical development, this book should be of service to those concerned with development, applications research, technical service, market research, commercial development and manufacturing, as well as to those who desire a practical introduction to the subject.

This second edition incorporates much new material. The introductory chapter was completely rewritten, as was the one on ethylene oxide polymers. A new chapter, "Polyethylenimine," was added, and the chapter on alkyl and hydroxyalkylcellulose derivatives was replaced by two chapters, "Methyl- and Hydroxypropyl Methyl-Cellulose Derivatives" and "Hydroxyethylcellulose," to better cover this important area of water-soluble resins. Each of the other chapters was revised, extensively in some cases.

The principal objectives of this revised edition of "Water-soluble Resins" are to stimulate new and imaginative thought toward the application of water-soluble resin technology and to effect the transfer of stimulating ideas between different industry and application areas. The following is a partial list of water-soluble resins applications that indicates the breadth of potential technology and the opportunities for cross-fertilization of ideas:

- *Adhesives:* Remoistenable adhesive compounds; aqueous thickeners
- *Beverages:* Clarification
- *Ceramics:* Clay binders; glazing formulations
- *Cosmetics:* Hair sprays; lotions; ointment formulations
- *Detergents:* Anti-redeposition agents; builders
- *Explosives:* Binders
- *Fertilizers:* Binders; granulating agents
- *Food Products:* Thickeners; stabilizers; humectants; emulsifying aids
- *Glass:* Binders for glass fibers
- *Latex Coatings:* Thickeners; pigment suspending agents
- *Leathers:* Adhesives; leather drying
- *Metallurgy:* Binders for magnesium oxide treatment of electrical steel
- *Minerals Processing:* Flocculants for settlings fines
- *Paper:* Coating binders; clay flocculants; surface sizes
- *Petroleum Production:* Water loss agents; drilling mud additives
- *Pharmaceuticals:* Thickeners; suspending agents
- *Plastics:* Protective colloids for emulsion polymerization
- *Rubber:* Release agents for rubber products
- *Textiles:* Warp size agents

In addition, water-soluble resins are used in agricultural chemicals, building materials, cements, asphalts, emulsifiers, lithography, lubricants, packaging, paints, photographic films, toiletries, and a host of chemical specialties.

The editors wish to express their appreciation for the enthusiasm of the authors who prepared various chapters in this book, and for the cooperation of their respective companies in opening their data files for publication.

May, 1968

Robert L. Davidson
Marshal Sittig

Contents

A. T. Anderson

Market Area Manager
Chemical Market Development
Chemicals and Plastics Development Division
Union Carbide Corporation
New York, New York

1

Introduction

Water-soluble polymers are not the most glamorous of plastics. They are not in the public eye as are the more exotic plastic products, such as nose cones for missiles, nylon for paint brushes, polyvinyl chloride for cosmetic jars and bottles, and polystyrene handles for toothbrushes. Yet these water-soluble polymers perform essential functions in latex paints, cosmetics, and toothpastes — even laxatives.

This lack of public awareness, however, does not change the fact that the water-soluble polymer business represents a sizable and steadily growing segment of the plastics industry. Last year, more than 3 billion pounds of water-soluble polymers were consumed, valued at more than $400 million. Consumption will probably grow at the rate of 1.3 per cent per year.

However, the size of the market in terms of dollars and the rate of growth are deceptive for two reasons: (1) The great bulk of the water-soluble polymers consumed are starches, which sell for 5 to 10 cents per pound; (2) The water-soluble polymer business comprises three distinct product categories — natural products, modified natural products, and synthetic products.

Last year, the market for modified natural and synthetic water-soluble polymers was well over 125 million pounds per year, worth almost $90 million, and is growing at the rate of 7.8 per cent per year (see Figure 1.1). And the production capacity for these water-soluble polymers was 202 million pounds per year (see Table 1.1).

WHERE WATER-SOLUBLE POLYMERS ARE USED

Natural Products

These are derived from animal and vegetable sources, and have been marketed for many years. They represent by far the largest volume of sales in the water-soluble polymer area. These polymers are typified by such

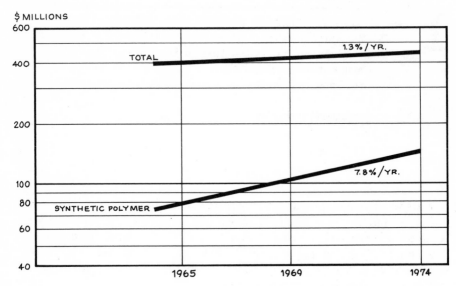

FIGURE 1.1   The market for water-soluble polymers.

materials as the starches, dextrins, alginates, natural gums, gelatin, glue, and casein.

Modified Natural Products

Compounds produced by altering the chemical structure of natural products have been around almost as long as the natural products. The number of entries in this area is increasing steadily. This class of water-soluble polymer is represented by the alkyl- and hydroxyalkyl ethers of cellulose and starch, ionic starches — starch sulfates, sulfonates, and carboxylates — carboxymethylcelluloses, and the mixed ethers of starch and cellulose.

Synthetic Products

These are the latest members of the water-soluble polymer family. Included in this category are materials such as polyvinyl alcohols, polyvinylpyrrolidones, polyvinylmethyl ethers, polyacrylic acid and its salts, polyacrylamides, ethylene oxide polymers, and various copolymer systems.

As mentioned above, the total water-soluble polymer market will grow slowly at the rate of 1.3 per cent per year, while the synthetic and modified natural polymer segment will grow more rapidly at the rate of 7.8 per cent per year. The latter polymers have grown and will continue to grow at a higher rate because they are not only displacing the natural polymers in many applications, but are also creating entirely new end-use areas. Even though higher priced, they are replacing natural products because of:

Greater Efficiency — Much lower dosages are needed to do a given job.

Increased Versatility — They can be tailored to better serve a given need.

Lower Biological Oxygen Demand — Important where stream pollution is a critical consideration.

FUNCTIONS OF WATER-SOLUBLE POLYMERS

For industrial applications, synthetic and modified natural polymers serve many functions, as can be seen readily in Figure 1.2. About 53 per cent

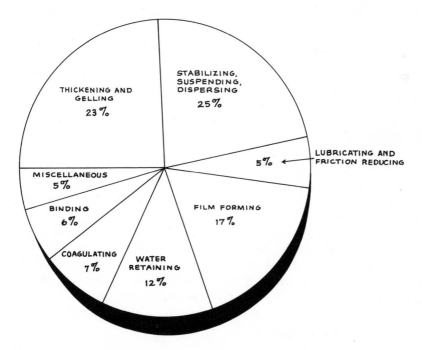

FIGURE 1.2 How synthetic water-soluble polymers are used.

of all water-soluble polymers are used to thicken and stabilize water-based products. Hydroxyethylcellulose and methylcellulose are examples of thickening and gelling agents that are applied in such products as latex paints and cosmetics. Polymers commonly used as stabilizing, suspending, or dispersing agents for water insoluble solids or liquids are hydroxyethyl-cellulose and polyvinyl alcohol in emulsion polymerization and carboxymethylcellulose in drilling muds, in paper manufacture, or in detergent formulations as a soil suspending aid.

About 17 per cent of all water-soluble polymers are used as film forming agents. Typical examples are polyvinyl alcohol and polyethylene oxide for packaging films, or carboxymethylcellulose for textile warp-sizing. Water retention aids include polyethylene oxide and methylcellulose for cement-asbestos extrusion, or hydroxyethylcellulose for oil well cements. Typical coagulants for suspended solids or liquids are the polyacrylamides for water treatment uses. Carboxymethylcellulose and methylcellulose are representative binding agents — the former for welding rods and the latter for toothpaste.

PROPERTIES OF WATER-SOLUBLE POLYMERS

Electrochemical Behavior

Water-soluble polymers exhibit three types of electrochemical behavior:

Nonionic — Polymers that do not ionize in water solution are classified as nonionic polymers. Most water-soluble polymers fall into this category, including starches, ethyl hydroxyethylcellulose, hydroxyethylcellulose, and polyethylene glycols.

Anionic — This category comprises the second largest number of water-soluble polymers. Anionic polymers ionize in aqueous solution to produce a polymeric species bearing a negative charge. Among those polymers possessing this ionic character are sodium carboxymethylcellulose, polyacrylic acid salts, and alginates.

Cationic — Only four commercially available water-soluble polymers exhibit cationic behavior — three are natural products. The resultant polymeric species upon ionization in water solution possesses a positive charge. Acrylamide copolymers (the only cationic synthetic), guar gum, starch derivatives, and casein display this cationic behavior.

Rheological Behavior

Water-soluble polymers may be divided into four categories depending on their viscosity response to an applied force in aqueous media. These four rheological classes are *newtonian flow, pseudoplastic flow, dilatent flow,* and *thixotropic flow.*

Viscosity is the measure of the resistance of a liquid to flow. More exactly, it is defined as the ratio of the shearing stress to the rate of shearing:

$$\text{Viscosity} = \frac{\text{Shear Stress}}{\text{Shear Rate}}$$

The shear stress is the resistance of the liquid to flow under the influence of an applied force — the molecular resistance within a body opposing an external force. It is defined as:

$$\text{Shear Stress} = \frac{\text{Force}}{\text{Area Sheared}} = \text{Dynes/cm}^2$$

When a liquid is sheared, assuming laminar flow, the layers of the liquid move at different rates. The relative rate of motion of the layers is only one factor in the rate of shear. The other is the distance, or clearance, between the shearing planes. Mathematically the shear rate is defined as:

$$\text{Shear Rate} = \frac{\text{Velocity}}{\text{Clearance}} = \frac{\text{cm/sec}}{\text{cm}} = \frac{1}{\text{sec}} = \text{sec}^{-1}$$

Therefore, from the first equation, viscosity has the following dimensions:

$$\text{Viscosity} = \frac{\text{Shear Stress}}{\text{Shear Rate}} = \frac{\dfrac{\text{Dynes}}{\text{cm}^2}}{\dfrac{1}{\text{sec}}} = \frac{\text{Dynes/sec}}{\text{cm}^2} = \text{poise}$$

Newtonian flow   In this type of system, the viscosity is not dependent upon time or shear rate. It is, however, dependent upon solution concentration and temperature. Solutions of high polymers are very rarely Newtonian. Their viscosities depend upon the manner in which they are used or measured.

In Newtonian flow, the shear rate is directly proportional to the applied shearing stress. The proportionality constant — viscosity — remains constant with the shear rate. Newtonian flow is approached in very dilute polymer solutions or in solutions of very low molecular weight polymers.

Pseudoplastic flow   Most polymer solutions of moderate concentrations exhibit pseudoplastic flow. The shear rate exhibits a higher than first order relationship with respect to the applied stress, and the viscosity decreases with increasing shear rate. Ethyl hydroxyethylcellulose, hydroxyethylcellulose, sodium carboxymethylcellulose, polyethylene oxide, polyvinyl alcohol, and alginates are examples of water-soluble polymers that demonstrate pseudoplasticity.

Dilatent flow   Dilatency is seldom encountered except in dispersions having about 50 per cent solids. It involves an increase in viscosity with increasing shear rate. In such systems, the volume fraction of solvent coincides with the combined volume of all the interparticle voids; the amount of solvent is sufficient to coat and lubricate the particles. Shearing disturbs the particle order causing the particle to occupy a larger volume and exposing dry surfaces which cause an apparent increase in viscosity. Starch is the only water-soluble polymer that exhibits dilatent flow.

Thixotropic flow   This rheological behavior involves a decrease in viscosity as a function of time. Thixotropic systems re-establish their "structure" upon standing undisturbed. Thixotropic flow never exists alone; it is always a superposition of the viscosity-time relationship upon one of the previously described flow types. Most common is the thixotropic-pseudoplastic flow combination. For example, solutions of sodium carboxymethylcellulose, cellulose ether, hydroxyethylcellulose, and sodium carboxymethyl hydroxyethylcellulose can be thixotropic and pseudoplastic.

Processable Polymers

An increasingly important marketing tool in the water-soluble polymer business is the ability to tailor a polymer to specific applications. This is one of the major reasons why synthetic water-soluble polymers are growing at a faster rate than natural products. Ethylene-maleic anhydride copolymers and polyvinylpyrrolidone are two examples of polymers that can be processed to suit specific needs.

The *ethylene-maleic anhydride* resin series is based on the chemically reactive maleic anhydride-ethylene copolymer system which is in effect a macromolecular chemical intermediate. It is commercially available in, or readily converted to, a variety of derivatives — each having different solution characteristics. They are offered as linear polymers as well as a cross-linked microgels based on the same parent copolymer base.

The linear copolymers are of low and intermediate molecular weight and are frequently used as film formers, emulsifying agents, thickening agents, and protective colloids. These resins are completely soluble in water and yield clear solutions which range from essentially Newtonian to highly pseudoplastic flow.

The cross-linked polymers dissolve to yield rather clear dispersions of highly swollen microgels, which exhibit unusual and highly useful solution properties. The confinement of electrostatic repulsion, by incorporating an appropriate low percentage of cross-links, allows each microgel to swell enormously, imbibe tremendous volumes of solvent and act as a miniature spherical membrane.

These membranes can swell to contain several thousand times their weight in bound solvent. The result is a crowded network of clear microgels which has many desirable features. Such features include extremely high thickening efficiency at low concentrations, gel strength at low concentrations, and excellent retention of solution viscosity with increasing temperature.

Polyvinylpyrrolidone is the classic example of a nonionic high molecular weight polymer compatible with an extremely broad spectrum of systems. The product versatility, which ranges from such applications as a synthetic blood plasma to its use as an auxiliary for rag dye stripping, is dependent upon the almost universal complexing ability of the incorporated monomer rather than on the molecular weight or physical shape of the polymer chain. This versatility is primarily a function of the heterocyclic, carbonyl-containing 2-pyrrolidone pendent group attached to every other carbon atom on the main chain.

APPLICATIONS OF WATER-SOLUBLE POLYMERS

Water-soluble polymers are used in a variety of market areas as outlined in Figure 1.3 and Table 1.2. Detergents and laundry products head the list accounting for about 16 per cent of the total market. Typical products for

TABLE 1.1. Synthetic and Modified Natural Water-Soluble Polymers.

Polymer	Number of Producers	Total Capacity, lb
Poly(vinyl alcohol)	5	68,000,000
Carboxymethylcellulose	5	58,000,000
Methylcellulose and cellulose ethers	3	30,000,000
Hydroxyethylcellulose	2	20,000,000
Polyacrylamides	3	9,000,000
Poly(vinlypyrrolidone)	1	4,000,000
Poly(ethylene oxide)	1	2,000,000
Maleic anhydride copolymers	2	6,000,000
Poly(acrylic acid)	2	5,000,000
Polyethylenimine	2	2,000,000
Total	15*	204,000,000

* Several producers make more than one water-soluble polymer.

this application are carboxymethylcellulose and maleic anhydride copolymers.

Examples of polymers used in other market areas are: carboxymethylcellulose and polyvinyl alcohol in textiles; polyvinyl alcohol in adhesives; carboxymethylcellulose and methylcellulose in food products; polyacrylamides and polyethylenimine in paper; hydroxyethylcellulose and methylcellulose in paints; and polyethylene oxide and polyvinylpyrrolidone in pharmaceuticals and cosmetics.

TABLE 1.2. General Properties and End Uses of Synthetic and Natural Water-Soluble Polymers.

LEGEND:
G = Gels made by use of additives
AG = Gels formed by aging
TG = Thermal gelation
TAG = Thermal aging gelation

Viscosity Ranges Low Shear: XL = Extra Low, M = Medium, XH = Extra High

Product	U.S.A. 1966 Use, MM lb	U.S.A. 1966 Price, $/lb	Anionic (−)	Cationic (+)	Nonionic (0)	No. of Grades and Types Offered	FDA-Approved, Food	Dilatent	Thixotropic	Pseudoplastic	Viscosity Ranges Low Shear	Organics	Hot Water	Cold Water	Gelation	Biodegradable
SYNTHETIC PRODUCTS																
Cellulose Derivatives																
Cellulose ether ("Klucel")					X	7			X	X	XL-L-M-H-XH	X		X	TG	X
Ethyl hydroxyethylcellulose					X	3				X	H-M-L	X		X	TG	X
Ethyl methylcellulose					X	—					—	X	X			X
Hydroxyethylcellulose	9.5	0.69			X	75			X	X	XL-L-M-H-XH			X		X
Hydroxyethyl methylcellulose					X	18					—			X	TG	X
Hydroxypropyl methylcellulose	27.0	0.69			X	17	X				L-M-H	X		X	TG	X
Methylcellulose					X	24	X				L-M-H			X	TG	X
Sodium carboxymethylcellulose	65.0	.40–.59	X				X		X	X	XL-L-M-H-XH		X	X		X
Sodium carboxymethyl hydroxyethylcellulose			X						X	X			X	X		X
Sodium cellulose sulfate			X								L-M-H		X	X		X
Acrylates																
Polyacrylic acid salts	3.4	0.60	X			2					L		X	X	G	
Polyacrylamide	6.6	1.55			X	1					L-M		X	X		
Acrylamide copolymers	0.7	0.75	X	X	X	3					L		X	X		
Miscellaneous																
Carboxyvinyl polymer ("Carbopol")	1.3	2.50	X			1	X			X	H	X		X		
Polyethylene glycols	36.4	.24–.35			X	9					L-M	X	X	X		
Polyethylene oxide	2.0	.60–1.25			X	8					L-M-H-XH	X	X	X		
Polyvinyl alcohol	33.8	.47–.86			X	14				X	L		X	X		
Polyvinyl methyl ether		.65–.81			X	4				X	L	X		X		
Polyvinylpyrrolidone	16.9	1.50			X	4					L	X	X	X	AG	

NATURAL PRODUCTS																	
Exudates from Vegetation																	
Gum arabic	36.4	.22–.45	X			9	X				L		X	X	X	G	X
Gum karaya	5.2	.25–.48		X	X	9	X				H		X	X	X	G	X
Gum tragacanth	1.1	.60–4.00		X	X	12	X				L-M-H		X	X	X		X
Seed Extractives																	
Guar gum	50.0	.26–.34	X	X	X	125	X			X	M-H-XH		X	X	X		X
Locust bean gum	6.8	.32–.35		X	X	3	X				H		X	X	X	TAG	X
Starch	2675.0	0.06	X	X	X	7	X	X			L		X	X	X	TAG	X
Starch derivatives	900.0	0.08		X	X	20	X		X	X	L		X	X	X		X
Proteins (Soy)	—	.23–.25		X	X	—	X				L		X	X	X		X
Seaweed Products																	
Agar-agar	0.5	2.50	X			5	X				M		X	X	X	G	X
Alginates	12.0	.92–1.90	X		X	5	X			X	L-M-H		X	X	X	G	X
Irish moss	40.0	.23–1.75			X	2	X				M		X	X	X		X
Animal Origin																	
Casein	103.2	0.25	X	X	X	5	X				L		X	X	X		X
Gelatin	73.0	0.57		X	X	2	X				L		X	X	X	TG	X

TABLE 1.2. General Properties and End Uses of Synthetic and Natural Water-Soluble Polymers (cont'd).

1 = Most important use
2 = Second most important use
3 = Third most important use
X = Other end uses mentioned by manufacturer

GENERAL END-USE RANKINGS

	Adhesives	Agriculture	Asphalt	Caulking	Ceramics	Concrete	Cosmetics	Detergents	Electrical	Film	Fire-fighting	Flocculation	Foundries	Food	Glass Fiber	Ink	Joint Cement	Latex	Leather	Metallurgical	Mining	Mortars	Oil Wells	Paint	Paint Remover	Paper	Photography	Pharmaceutical	Plating	Rubber	Textile Print Paste	Textile Size	Textile Finishing	Tobacco	Wallboard	Wallpaper
SYNTHETIC PRODUCTS																																				
Cellulose Derivatives																																				
Cellulose ether ("Klucel")	X		2				X											X						X	1											
Ethyl hydroxyethylcellulose			2							X								X						X												
Ethyl methylcellulose																																				
Hydroxyethylcellulose	X	X	X		X	X	X	X	X				X		X	X			X		X	X	3			X	X	X	X	X	X			X	X	X
Hydroxyethyl methylcellulose		X	X		X	X	X	X										2						1									X	X	X	X
Hydroxypropyl methylcellulose	X	X	X	X	X	X	1	X	X		X			2		X	X	X	X		X	X	X	3	X	X	X	X	X	X	X	X	X	X		
Methylcellulose		X	X	X	X	X	3	X						1		X		X	X		X	X	X	2		X		X		X	X	X	X	X	X	X
Sodium carboxymethylcellulose	X	X	X	X	X	X	1	1					X	2					X	X		X	3	X		X	X	X		X	X	X	X	X	X	X
Sodium carboxymethyl hydroxyethylcellulose													X			X								X		X	X									
Sodium cellulose sulfate										X								X																		
Acrylates																																				
Polyacrylic acid salts	2									X								3	X	X				X					X				1			
Polyacrylamide		X			X	X		X	X			X			X	X	X		X	X				X		X			X							
Acrylamide copolymers	X	X			X	X		X	X			X			X	X	X		X	X				X												
Miscellaneous																																				
Carboxyvinyl polymer ("Carbopol")	3	X	X				1	X						2									X	X	X	X		X		X	X					
Polyethylene glycols	X	X			X		1																	X	X			3	X	X	X	2	X			
Polyethylene oxide	X	X										2			X			X				X	1	X	X	3	X	3				X	X			
Polyvinyl alcohol	1	X			X	X				1						X	X	X						1	X	X	X				X	X	X		X	
Polyvinyl methyl ether	X				X										X	X	X	X					X	X						X	X	2	X			
Polyvinylpyrrolidone	3	X					1	X			X					X		X	X					X		X		2		X	X	X	X			

NATURAL PRODUCTS																																				
Exudates from Vegetation																																				
Gum arabic	X	X			X		3							1		X										X		X	2			X	X			
Gum karaya		X					3							2												X		1			X					
Gum tragacanth		X				X	3							1					X										2		X		X	X		
Seed Extractives																																				
Guar gum	X	X	X	X	X		X					X		1					X		X			X				X			X	X	X			X
Locust bean gum	X				X			X						1					X					X		X		2			X	X	X			
Starch	X												X	1												2						3				
Starch derivatives	X				X							X	X						X				X			1		X				2				
Proteins (Soy)	3															X		X						2		1									X	X
Seaweed Products																																				
Agar-agar	X	X					3							1					X		X					X	2	X				X				
Alginates	X	X	X		X		2				X	X		1			3		X					X			X			X	X	X		X		
Irish moss														1														2								
Animal Origin																																				
Casein	X													2										3		1										
Gelatin							X					X		1												X	3	2				X				

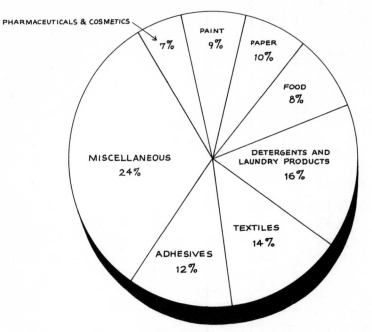

FIGURE 1.3   Market areas for synthetic water-soluble polymers.

Various other products are used in such diverse fields as oil well drilling operations, mineral ore processing, sewage and waste water treatment, and cements and mortars.

M. W. Rutenberg

Research Department
National Starch and Chemical Corporation
Plainfield, New Jersey

2

Modified Starches

This chapter is concerned with modified starches of commercial interest and the effect of modification upon the basic properties of the native starches of commerce. Starch is used primarily because of its thickening, gelling, adhesive, and film-forming properties. This versatile combination of properties in conjunction with availability in large quantities, controlled quality, and low cost has resulted in widespread usage of starch. However, this alone is not sufficient to meet the stringent demands of today's complex technology which requires specific combinations of properties tailored to particular processes and products. Hence, the modification of starch to impart new properties, to improve some of its inherent properties, or to repress others is necessary. These modifications result in the introduction of new chemical groups and/or changes in the size, shape, and organization of the starch molecules. To use modified starches effectively, it is essential to have some knowledge of the basic properties of the native starches and to understand, thereby, the effects of modification.[1]

STRUCTURE AND PROPERTIES OF NATIVE STARCHES

Starch usage is based mainly upon the physical properties of its aqueous dispersions and the films prepared from them. These properties are a reflection of the chemical composition, molecular architecture, and molecular organization. The behavior of the native starches can therefore be interpreted in terms of chemical structure and organization.

Starch is a substance of definite chemical composition which occurs widely as the reserve food in most land plants. Since these plants store starch in a number of different forms, the starch from different plant sources

---

[1] For more details on the theoretical and industrial aspects of starch and its modification, see "Starch: Chemistry and Technology," R. L. Whistler and E. F. Paschall, eds., Academic Press, N.Y., Volume I, 1965, Volume II, 1967. "Methods In Carbohydrate Chemistry," R. L. Whistler, ed., Academic Press, N.Y., 1964, Volume IV, gives methods for preparation, analysis, and physical characterization of starch and modified starches.

will vary somewhat in physical properties. Hence, various native starches exist, each designated by its plant source (e.g., cornstarch, rice starch, tapioca starch).

Chemical Composition

Starch belongs to the class of organic compounds called carbohydrates and is composed of carbon, hydrogen, and oxygen in the ratio $C_6 H_{10} O_5$. These atoms are organized into a simple sugar molecule, D-glucose, or dextrose as it is known commercially (Figure 2.1a). The glucose molecules are,

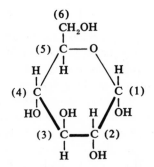

(a) Dextrose (D-glucose) showing numbering of carbon atoms.

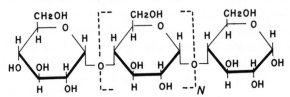

(b) Linear chain structure of the starch molecule. Each hexagonal group represents a dextrose unit. "N" is the number of dextrose units in the chain.

FIGURE 2.1   The chemical structure of starch.

in turn, united to form large starch molecules. Thus, starch is a polymer made up of a large number of glucose units.

The glucose units are connected through an oxygen atom joining carbon atom number one of one glucose unit to carbon atom number four of the next glucose unit, making a long chain as shown in Figure 2.1b. The polymer chemist would consider starch a condensation polymer of glucose formed by elimination of water between glucose units. Hence, the glucose units in the starch chain are really anhydroglucose units since one molecule of water is missing from each unit.

It is evident from the structure of starch that modification can take place at the hydroxyl groups (—OH) through reactions such as oxidation, esterification, or ether-formation. The linkages between the glucose units in the chain will be recognized as acetal linkages by the organic chemist and thus subject to scission by acid hydrolysis, leading to cutting of the chain (depolymerization). When this depolymerization reaction is carried all the way, corn sugar or dextrose is obtained.

Commercial starches contain very small amounts of proteins, fats, and phosphates, depending on the variety.

Molecular Architecture

Since molecules are three-dimensional structures, a glance at Figure 2.1a will show that the hydroxyl groups and hydrogen atoms may lie in space above or below the hexagonal ring made up of carbon atoms 1 to 5 and the ring oxygen atom. In the Figure, if the ring is visualized as projecting out of the paper, with the heavy lines at the bottom closest to the reader and the top of the hexagonal ring pushing through the page to the other side, then the hydroxyl groups and hydrogen atoms above the ring lines will be above the ring in space, and those below the ring lines will be below the ring in space.

The relative arrangement in space of the hydroxyl group on carbon atom number two and the oxygen atom connecting carbon atom number one to the next glucose unit is the major structural difference between starch and cellulose, which are both composed of chains of D-glucose units. In starch, it is seen from Figure 2.1b that this oxygen atom lies on the same side of the hexagon (below) as the C-2 hydroxyl group (*cis*). This spatial arrangement is known as the "alpha-linkage" (α).

In cellulose this oxygen link between glucose units is on the opposite side of the ring (above) from the C-2 hydroxyl group (*trans*), and this relationship is known as the "beta-linkage" (β). This seemingly small difference in the spatial arrangement of the atoms in the molecule is the major factor which accounts for the differences in the properties of starch and cellulose.

Starch occurs in two structural forms: a linear polymer called amylose and a highly branched, tree-like polymer termed amylopectin. Amylose and cellulose are chemically and architecturally similar, as mentioned above, both being made up of glucose and both being linear molecules. Amylopectin is considered to be composed of glucose chains similar to amylose but with many branch points. The attachment of branch chains by oxygen links between carbon atom number one of one glucose unit to carbon atom number six of a glucose unit already in a chain is the main point of branching. These branch points are believed to occur at intervals of about 20 to 25 glucose

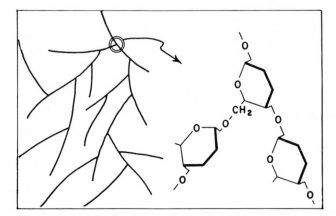

FIGURE 2.2   The structure of the branched fraction of starch (at left) with the chemical configuration of the circled branch point (at right). (*Corn Starch,* 2d ed., 1958, Corn Industries Research Foundation, Inc., now Corn Refiners Association, Inc., Washington, D.C.)

units. This structure is shown in Figure 2.2. There also appears to be a minor amount of branch linkages at carbon atom number three.

The size of the amylose and amylopectin molecules varies with the plant source and the method used to isolate them. The estimates of molecular weight are also very much dependent upon the method of measurement (light scattering, sedimentation, osmotic pressure, end-group). The molecular weight of amylose has been estimated at roughly 40,000 to 340,000, corresponding to chains containing 250 to 2100 glucose monomeric units (degree of polymerization of 250 to 2100). The highly branched amylopectin is a very large molecule with molecular weight estimates as high as 75 to 100 million. It appears to have a very broad distribution of molecular weight. In general, the amylose and amylopectin from white potato starch have higher molecular weights than these fractions from cornstarch.

Much of the behavior of starch can be traced to the affinity of the hydroxyl groups in one molecule for those in another. In linear polymers like cellulose and amylose, the straight chains can orient in parallel alignment so that a large number of the hydroxyl groups along one chain are in close proximity to those on adjacent chains. When this happens, the hydroxyl groups form associations through hydrogen bonds and the chains are bound together forming aggregates which are insoluble in water. In very dilute solutions, the aggregated chains of amylose will precipitate; in more concentrated solutions, a gel will form (Figure 2.3).

This process of alignment, association, and precipitation or gelling is

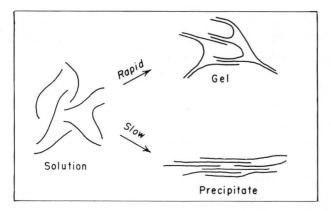

FIGURE 2.3 Mechanisms of starch retrogradation. Rapid retrogradation of a concentrated paste gives a gel; slow retrogradation of a dilute solution gives a precipitate. (*Corn Starch*, 2d ed., 1958. Corn Industries Research Foundations, Inc., now Corn Refiners Association, Inc., Washington, D.C.)

known as retrogradation. Retrogradation is essentially a crystallization process and is a very important factor in the modification and usage of starch. Because of the linearity of amylose and its marked tendency to form associated aggregates, this material is insoluble in water and forms strong, flexible films.

On the other hand, the highly branched chains of the amylopectin molecules cannot align and associate so readily. Consequently amylopectin tends to be soluble, forming solutions that will not gel under normal conditions. On prolonged aging or under special conditions (e.g., freezing), some retrogradation effects can be observed in dispersions containing amylopectin. It should be noted that the hydroxyl groups also tend to attract and hold water molecules through the same association forces.

Granular Packaging

Starch is obtained in a unique natural package which is distinctive to the plant that produces it. The molecules of amylose and amylopectin are organized and packed into small granules which vary in size and shape depending on the plant source (Figure 2.4). The relative proportions of amylose and amylopectin in the granule will also vary with the plant source, most common root and grain starches containing 17 to 28 per cent amylose (see Table 2.1).

This unique granular package, which holds a water-soluble polymer in an

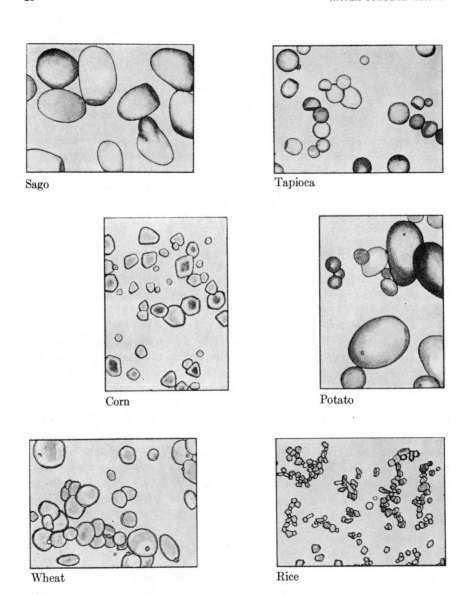

FIGURE 2.4 Microscopic appearance of different types of starch granules with 400× magnification. [*The Story of Starches*, 1953, National Starch Products, Inc. (now National Starch and Chemical Corporation).]

insoluble form, is a primary factor in accounting for the economic usefulness of starch. The starch can be extracted from the plant materials, purified, and modified in an aqueous slurry and then recovered by filtration and dry-

TABLE 2.1. Starch Granule Characteristics.

Starch	Granule Size[a] (Microns)		Granule Shape	Amylose (Per Cent)	Gelatinization Temperature[b]	
					5% Solution (°F)	33⅓% Solution (°F)
Corn	4–26	(15)	Round, polygonal	29	176	156
Waxy corn	5–25	(15)	Round, polygonal	0–6	165	162
Potato	15–100	(33)	Oval	23	147	142
Tapioca	5–36	(20)	Truncated, round, oval	18	145	136
Sago	15–65		Oval, truncated	27	165	160
Wheat	2–38	(20–22)	Oval, round	25	170	140
Rice	3–9	(5)	Polygonal	17	178	167

[a] 1 micron = 0.001 millimeter = 0.000394 inches. Average size given in parentheses.
[b] "Story of Starches," National Starch Products Inc., 1953 (National Starch and Chemical Corporation).

ing. It can be handled as a high-solids, pumpable, aqueous slurry until its thickening, adhesive, or film-forming properties are required. Then on heating the aqueous slurry, a temperature is reached (140 to 180F) at which the starch granules swell and rupture, yielding a viscous colloidal dispersion with concurrent release of some starch molecules into solution. Starch may also be dispersed in water at room temperature using certain alkalies (e.g., sodium hydroxide, benzyltrimethylammonium hydroxide), salts in high concentration (e.g., potassium iodide, calcium chloride, sodium salicylate, potassium thiocyanate), or organic dispersing agents (e.g., urea dicyanodiamide). In place of water, starch can be dispersed in other solvents such as dimethylsulfoxide or liquid ammonia.

Cooking Characteristics

Modifications of native starches are carried out to adapt their basic properties to specific use requirements. The properties concerned are gelatinization characteristics, viscosity, tendency of dispersions to gel, and the colloidal behavior of dispersions. A general picture of these characterizing properties can be obtained from the cooking and cooling curves which plot viscosity changes with temperature variations.

The curves in Figure 2.5 show the changes which take place with corn, potato, and waxy-maize starches on heating and cooling. When a starch suspension in water is heated, no effect on viscosity is noted until the gelatinization temperature is reached. This is the temperature at which the

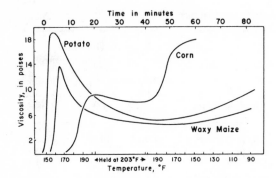

FIGURE 2.5 Cooking-cooling curves of potato, corn, and waxy-maize (amioca) starches heated to 203F and then cooled. Concentration of cornstarch is 35 grams in 450 cubic centimeters of water; potato and waxy-maize starches are at 25 grams in 450 cubic centimeters of water. (*Corn Starch*, 2d ed., 1958. Corn Industries Research Foundation, Inc., now Corn Refiners Association, Inc., Washington, D.C.)

granules begin to swell, hydrating rapidly and taking up a greater proportion of the available space in the slurry. This leads to a noticeable increase in the viscosity of the mixture as the swelling of the granules (gelatinization) progresses.

Cornstarch thins slightly as cooking continues at elevated temperature. On cooling, the hot colloidal dispersion increases markedly in viscosity and eventually forms a gel. This tendency to increase in viscosity and gel is attributed to the retrogradation of the amylose which has diffused into solution. A starch dispersion that sets to a firm, semirigid, jelly-like mass (gel) is said to be unstable; one that remains as a fluid sol is considered stable.

Evidently potato starch and waxy-maize starch gelatinize at a lower temperature than cornstarch, reach a higher peak viscosity, and break down or thin out considerably more than the cornstarch on continued heating and stirring. The initial viscosity of starch pastes is produced by the swollen granules. As cooking and agitation continue, these fragile, swollen granule masses tend to break down, releasing starch molecules into solution. The resulting colloidal dispersion is a complex mixture of swollen granular masses, ruptured granules, hydrated molecular aggregates, and dissolved molecules.

The potato and waxy-maize starch granules are more fragile or more readily broken down than those of cornstarch, hence the more rapid breakdown from the initial peak viscosity. Both waxy-maize and potato starch pastes thicken (set back) much less than cornstarch pastes. In the case of waxy maize, little or no amylose is present to retrograde. The increased stability of potato starch has been attributed to the presence of some branching in the amylose and to its larger molecular size. Tapioca starch behaves similarly.

The cooking-cooling characteristics of the various unmodified starches are affected by concentration, temperature of cooking, type and speed of agitation, pH, and the presence of additives such as sugar and salts. These characteristics are important in determining which of the native starches are suitable for a specific use and under what conditions. In those applications where a raw starch is unsuitable, a modified starch may be developed that will meet requirements.

STARCH SUPPLIES AND PRICES

Starch is commercially extracted from grains (corn, sorghum, wheat, rice), from roots or tubers (potato, cassava or tapioca, arrowroot), and from the pith of the sago palm. In the United States, cornstarch accounts for by far the largest share of starch production and sales. In 1966, the corn wet-milling industry, comprising eleven companies, processed about 210 million bushels of corn (and sorghum), equivalent to about 7 billion pounds of starch. Only about 40 per cent of this was offered as starch products, the remainder having been converted to corn syrup and sugar. Much smaller quantities of potato and wheat starches make up the remainder of domestic production. Additional starch supplies, comprising tapioca, sago, potato, arrowroot, corn, wheat, and rice starches, are available through import as shown in Table 2.2. Obviously, there is an abundant supply. The modified starches make up about 40 per cent of the total sales of cornstarch in the United States.

In recent years (1956 to 1966), the native starches have been priced at 5 to 12 cents per pound.[1] In the period 1954 to 1959, cornstarch showed little fluctuation in price, ranging from 6.19 to 6.59 cents per pound.[2] This price range has generally held through 1966. Powdered potato starch during the 1954 to 1959 period sold at 5.00 to 7.00 cents per pound.[2] In 1966, domestic potato starch was priced at 5.25 to 6.00 cents per pound; imports from Holland sold at about 7.50 cents per pound. Food grade tapioca (Thailand) which sold at 10 to 13.50 cents per pound in 1954 dropped to 5.25 to 6.30 cents per pound in 1959; similarly a medium industrial grade tapioca sold at

[1] All prices quoted in this chapter are carlots, f.o.b. United States point of shipment (imported starches, *ex* dock, N.Y.).

TABLE 2.2. U.S. Production & Imports of Starches.

Production (In millions of pounds)

	1964	1965	1966
Cornstarch[1]			
Starch[a]	2,677	2,823	2,942
Corn syrup[b]	2,799	2,846	2,947
Corn sugar, miscellaneous[b]	1,228	1,221	1,251
Total products	6,704	6,890	7,140
Potato starch[2]	18[c]	17[d]	106[e]
Wheat starch[3]	125	125	125
Total production	6,847	7,089	7,371
Imports (millions of pounds)[4]			
Tapioca[5]	294.4	358.0	340.7
Sago and Arrowroot[6]	4.3	4.9	3.0
Potato	8.1	28.5	1.5
Dextrin, miscellaneous starches[7]	23.6	25.5	33.6
Starch, miscellaneous[8]	17.8	29.2	23.0
Total imports	348.2	446.1	401.8

[1] Corn Refiners Association, Inc., Washington, D.C. Based on domestic and export shipments. Includes roughly 97 per cent of U.S. production (including sorghum).
[a] Includes pearl, acid-converted, oxidized, other modified starches, dextrins, and miscellaneous starch products.
[b] Manufacturers hydrolyzed the starch to syrup or sugar. The starch equivalent to the corn sugar would be 90 per cent of the amount shown. The starch equivalent to the syrup would be roughly 95 per cent of the amount shown.
[2] Potato starch is not estimated on a calendar year basis, but rather on a crop year basis. Harvesting the crop of a given year extends from January to about November 1st and the operating season (or "campaign") for manufacturing potato starch from the crop extends from October 1st to about June 1st of the following year. Thus, the actual manufacture of starch from a particular crop overlaps two years. Data presented here were obtained from estimates by Dr. R. H. Treadway, Eastern Utilization Research and Development Division, Agricultural Research Service, U.S. Department of Agriculture, Philadelphia, Pa. The estimates are based on the quantity of potatoes processed into starch and flour as given by "Irish Potatoes, Utilization of 1965 Crop with Comparisons," U.S. Dept. Agr., Crop Reporting Board, Statistical Reporting Service, Washington, D.C., September 8, 1966.
[c] Approximately 3 million hundredweights of potatoes from the 1964 crop were processed into starch and flour. Assuming 1.4 million cwts. for flour processing, and 11 per cent yield of starch from the remaining potatoes, approximately 18 million pounds of starch is estimated for the 1964 crop year. The low production reflects a small potato crop and high potato prices. Because of the poor crop it is likely that less than normal amounts of flour and more starch than estimated were manufactured in 1964. In the 1963 crop year 11.7 million cwts. were converted to starch and flour, yielding an estimated 113 million pounds of potato starch. U.S. Tariff Commission, Publication 179, "Summaries of Trade & Tariff Information," Vol. 6, Cereal Grains, Malts, Starches, and Animal Feeds, May 1966, p. 142 lists potato starch production in 1963 at 135 million pounds and in 1964 at 34 million pounds. These figures make no allowance for flour production and

5.15 to 8.20 cents per pound in 1954 and at 4.60 to 5.10 cents per pound in 1959.[1] High grade Siamese tapioca flour (Thailand) was priced at 5.35 to 6.25 cents per pound in 1966, with a low grade carrying a price of 4.65 to 5.40 cents per pound. Brazilian tapioca flour ranged in price from 5.45 to 6.75 cents per pound in 1966. In the same year, waxy cornstarch sold at 11 to 12 cents per pound while high amylose cornstarch was priced in the 15 to 18 cents per pound range. Most of the modified starches were selling at 7 to 12 cents per pound in 1966, depending on the type of starch and the particular modification. The more specialized derivatives were generally priced at less than 25 cents per pound in 1966. In a few cases, starch derivatives were quoted at higher than 25 cents per pound where newly developed products were being introduced.

MODIFICATION THROUGH PLANT BREEDING

The structure of synthetic polymers can be controlled and directed by selection of the conditions, catalysts, and reactants in the polymerization process. This results in polymers with specified properties. To do this with a natural polymer like starch, it is necessary to control the biological processes which produce the starch or develop plants that will synthesize the special polymer desired. This genetic approach is being explored to develop hybrids yielding starch containing only one form: linear amylose or branched amylopectin.

The waxy varieties of corn and milo maize (sorghum) were found to yield starch consisting almost entirely of amylopectin. Hybrid strains suitable for commercial planting and milling were developed and waxy starches have

[1] U.S. Tariff Commission Report No. 332–37, March, 1960, p. 84.

assume 11.5 per cent starch yield from potatoes. In the 1961 crop year, over 200 million pounds of potato starch were produced, a record.

[d] Estimated as in c above on basis of 8.1 million cwts. of potatoes converted to starch and flour.

[e] Estimated as in c, 11 million cwts. of potatoes converted to starch and flour. Statistical Reporting Service, U.S.D.A., September 7, 1967.

[3] Data not published. Annual production very roughly estimated (R. A. Anderson in "Starch, Chemistry and Technology," II, p. 61, op. cit.). In 1963, wheat and rice starch combined production was about 64 million pounds. (U.S. Tariff Commission, Publication 179, *op. cit.*, p. 136).

[4] *Source:* Bureau of Census, U.S. Dept. of Commerce. Data assembled by Corn Refiners Association, Inc., Washington, D.C.

[5] Includes tapioca and cassava starch and flour. Thailand, Brazil principal source.

[6] Includes starch and flour. Principal sources are Leeward and Windward Islands, Jamaica, Brazil.

[7] Includes dextrins, soluble starches, and chemically treated starches.

[8] Includes corn, rice, and wheat starches. Mainly corn starch.

been available commercially since 1942. As mentioned in a previous section, amylopectin shows little tendency to retrograde and therefore its dispersions tend to be stable and nongelling and its dried films are generally soluble in water. These properties found in the waxy starches make them useful in foods, textile finishing and printing, and in paper and paper products manufacture. The paste stability properties of the raw waxy starches carry over into their modifications.

At present a major effort is being made in university, government, and industrial laboratories to develop a hybrid corn containing starch that is composed entirely of amylose. A starch of this type would have a marked tendency to orient and associate (retrograde) and would therefore form strong, flexible films useful in packaging, coating, and sizing. Hybrids yielding starch containing up to 85 per cent amylose have been developed in experimental plant breeding work. Small commercial mill runs of a hybrid corn[1] containing 55 per cent amylose starch (versus 28 per cent amylose in regular cornstarch) were made in 1959 and 1960. Since that time, high amylose starch has been available in commercial quantities. Starches containing approximately 55 per cent and 70 per cent amylose are sold under the tradenames Amylomaize[2] (V and VII) and Amylon[3] (V and VII). Genetic work is continuing in the search for a 100 per cent amylose starch.

The high amylose cornstarch requires a much higher temperature to gelatinize than regular cornstarch, and therefore an aqueous slurry will not give as high a paste viscosity as an equal amount of regular cornstarch when both are cooked at 200F. Under these cooking conditions, the high amylose cornstarch granules will swell and hydrate somewhat. Essentially complete dispersions of high amylose cornstarch are obtained by batch autoclaving at 310 to 320F for about 15 minutes or by dispersing in $0.5N$ sodium hydroxide solution. Continuous high temperature commercial cookers, available through most starch producers, are excellent for preparing high amylose starch dispersions under commercial conditions.

The high amylose content of this starch results in high gel-strength pastes as well as good film properties. This strong gel-forming tendency of the high amylose starches is useful in the preparation of gum candies and snack foods. Extrusion processes have been used to prepare confectionery products from high amylose starch.[4] Various foods and confections may be coated by dipping into, or spraying with, dispersions of the high amylose starch.

Unsupported films have been prepared from solutions cast on metal belts or by extrusion of high solids dispersions formulated with plasticizers such

[1] Developed by the Bear Hydrid Corn Company, Decatur, Illinois.
[2] Product of American Maize-Products Company.
[3] Product of National Starch and Chemical Corporation.
[4] U.S. Patents 3,265,508–9.

as glycerol or sorbitol.[1] Starch films are almost impermeable to oxygen and nitrogen although they transmit water vapor. Unless these films are highly plasticized, they become brittle at low humidities. Starch films are discussed further in the next section on isolated amylose.

MODIFICATION THROUGH FRACTIONATION

A commercial method for fractionating potato starch into amylose and amylopectin was described in a Dutch patent issued to "Avebe" of Holland in 1955.[2] The method is based on dispersion of potato starch in an aqueous solution of magnesium sulfate (10 to 15 per cent) by autoclaving at 160C for about 15 minutes. On cooling to about 70C, the amylose precipitates preferentially and can be isolated and dried. Amylopectin precipitates on cooling to room temperature and can then be recovered.

Potato amylose is imported from Holland by Stein, Hall and Co., Inc., and is marketed in the United States and Canada at 30 cents per pound (1966) under the tradename Superlose.[3] Potato amylopectin, extracted in the process, is also available under the tradename "Ramalin"[3,4] at 20.5 cents per pound (1966).

These starches are not in granule form and hence the Ramalin is soluble in cold water, forming stable, viscous dispersions. On the other hand, the Superlose is insoluble because the amylose is in retrograded form. It can be dispersed by heating a slurry to approximately 320F in a continuous high temperature cooker or autoclave. About 2 to 5 minutes at this temperature will produce complete dispersion; longer times result in degradation with consequent reduced viscosity and film strength. These solutions gel quickly on cooling below a critical temperature which is dependent on the concentration (about 140F at 10 per cent concentration; higher temperature at higher concentration).

Retrogradation occurs more slowly when solutions of a given concentration are held at higher temperatures. Amylose solutions remain fluid for long periods by the addition of formaldehyde, which forms a hemiacetal with the amylose. This is an equilibrium which can be shifted to the original unstable amylose by decreasing the effective concentration of formaldehyde, by reaction with bisulfite, for example. Glyoxal will also act as a stabilizer for short time periods. The amylose can be solubilized in strong alkali solutions or in dimethylsulfoxide.

[1] U.S. Patent 3,243,308.
[2] U.S. patents 2,822,305; 2,829,987-8-9; 2,829,990. J. Muetgeert, Advances In Carbohydrate Chemistry, **16**, 299–333 (1961), Academic Press, N.Y.
[3] Product of Stein-Hall & Co., Inc.
[4] The A. E. Staley Manufacturing Co. has offered Nepol amylose and Magnapol amylopectin fractions made by a different process. U.S. patent 3,067,067.

The high temperature required for dispersing the amylose can be lowered and the tendency to retrograde can be reduced or eliminated by a suitable degree of derivatization. A balance of dispersibility in boiling water combined with insolubility in cold water is obtainable.[1] Various ethers and esters of amylose have been prepared.

Strong, transparent, flexible, colorless, unsupported films can be cast from amylose solutions. Films cast from unstabilized solutions are insoluble in water although they swell and lose strength. Films cast from formaldehyde-stabilized solution are water-sensitive but can be insolubilized by treatment to remove formaldehyde (sodium bisulfite, ammonia, etc.). These films can be treated further with cross-linking agents, such as glyoxal, urea-formaldehyde, etc., to obtain water insensitivity. The permeability of amylose film to water vapor, organic vapors, and gases is similar to that of cellophane.[2] Plasticizers for amylose films are of the class of sorbitol and glycerol.

Amylose or amylose acetate can form edible films which may be suitable for sausage casings or food packaging. Water-soluble films of amylose derivatives may be useful in the convenience packaging of detergents, food ingredients, bleaches, etc., where a unit package containing an exactly measured quantity is thrown directly into the washtub or processing vessel without additional preparations. The film properties of amylose are of value when the amylose is deposited on a substrate as a coating, size, or binder. The application areas for amylose are being actively explored and much of the technology must be worked out.

MODIFICATION BY CROSS-LINKING

The dispersibility and colloidal properties of starches can be modified by a relatively slight chemical treatment. The discussion on the properties of the starch granule pointed out that the gelatinization temperature, the initial paste viscosity, and the drop in viscosity on exposure to prolonged cooking, mechanical shear, or low pH were primarily due to the characteristics of the granule. By reinforcing the bonds holding the granule together, marked changes in the swelling behavior of the starch granule result.

This granule-toughening or inhibition is accomplished by cross-linking reactions via bifunctional reagents (e.g., epichlorohydrin, linear dicarboxylic acid anhydrides, organic dihalides, divinylsulfone, formaldehyde, phosphorus oxychloride, soluble metaphosphates, etc.) which form reinforcing links between the molecules in the granules. These cross-bonding reactions

[1] U.S. Patents 3,038,895; 3,122,534.
[2] J. C. Rankin, *et al.*, *Ind. Eng. Chem., Chem. Eng. Data Series*, **3**, 120–123 (1958).

apparently take place on or near the surface of the granule and, although the degree of cross-linking is very low (approximately one cross-link per 200 to 1000 glucose units), the effects on the dispersion characteristics of the treated starch are quite pronounced.

A starch, cross-bonded to this small extent, normally has a higher working viscosity for a given concentration than untreated starch. This is of value when thickening properties are required (adhesive for corrugated paperboard manufacture, textile printing, foods, pharmaceuticals). A slightly cross-linked starch has a slower rate of gelatinization making viscosity increase to maximum more gradual, the extent of this change being related to the degree of treatment. This property is useful where a delayed thickening on heating is desired, as in the retorting of canned foods.

The cross-linking treatment also increases the resistance of starch pastes to the thinning effects of prolonged agitation, heating, or exposure to acids or alkalies. Thus, the sharp rise to a peak viscosity followed by a rapid drop in viscosity given by some starches (e.g., potato, tapioca, waxy maize) can be eliminated by cross-bonding. This property is of interest in thickeners for canned foods where loss of viscosity on retorting is undesirable. It is also of importance where cooked starches are subjected to prolonged pumping and heating operations in processing while a uniform viscosity must be maintained.

A slight degree of cross-linking is particularly valuable in reducing the rubbery, cohesive character of tapioca, potato, and waxy-maize starch pastes to a smooth, creamy texture. These products, prepared with cross-linking reagents acceptable for modifying food starches,[1] are used in pie fillings, salad dressings, and puddings. Waxy starches of this type can withstand low-temperature storage in cooked form much better than any other starch developed to date and hence are choice materials for use in frozen foods.

The cross-linking reaction can be carried further. As the degree of cross-linking of ungelatinized starch granules is increased, they become more resistant to gelatinization. This can be carried to a point (about one cross-link in 20 glucose units) where the starch granule is completely resistant to normal cooking temperatures and can even be sterilized by autoclaving without becoming gelatinous. A product of this type is useful as a surgical dusting powder, particularly since material left in an incision is absorbed.

[1] Phosphorus oxychloride, epichlorohydrin, sodium trimetaphosphate, and adipic anhydride are acceptable under Food and Drug Administration Regulations when used at levels prescribed. Code of Federal Regulations, Title 21, Food and Drugs, Chapter I, Part 121, Subpart D, Food Additives Permitted in Food For Human Consumption, Section 121.1031 Food Starch-Modified, U.S. Government Printing Office, Washington, D.C.

CONVERTED STARCHES

The "thin-boiling" starches and dextrins of commerce are known as converted starches. They are prepared by degradation of starch molecules, yielding products of lower dispersion viscosity than the original raw starch. These products accounted for about 60 per cent of the total sales volume of modified cornstarch in 1966 compared to about 75 per cent in 1960. This indicates a relative increase in the sales volume of starch derivatives. The total sales of all modified corn starches (acid-converted, oxidized, dextrins, derivatives, and miscellaneous modified) increased from about 853 million pounds in 1960 to over one billion pounds in 1966. Sales of dextrins decreased somewhat from the 1959–1960 volume.

Converted cornstarches are low in cost and have maintained a stable price structure in recent years (1950 to 1966) in the range of 7 to 12 cents per pound, depending on the specific product. The prices of the corresponding tapioca and potato products are generally higher and fluctuate more.

These converted starches offer a wide range of film-forming, binding, and colloidal properties useful in many paper, textile, adhesive, and food processes and products. Depending on the type of converted product, variations in solubility, gel strength, tendency to gel, and viscosity are available. Viscosity is one of the most important factors influencing the use of water-soluble or dispersible materials; and it is necessary that these starches be available in a number of viscosity grades to meet varying applications requirements.

The conversion processes are applied mainly to reduce the viscosity of the raw starches. A low-viscosity product is of particular interest in uses where the properties of the dried film are needed. With a high-viscosity starch, a lower concentration of the starch in the dispersion is necessary to have a viscosity that is workable and can be applied by a particular machine. This low-solids dispersion requires the removal of large quantities of water to obtain the dry film (slower drying) thereby reducing machine speeds and depositing very thin films. Using converted starches, dispersions of higher concentration can be prepared while remaining within the workable viscosity limits of a particular machine operation or process; and the film laid down will dry faster and be thicker because less water will be present relative to the starch solids in the dispersion. An indication of the viscosity ranges of the raw and converted starches is shown in Figure 2.6.

The modification of starches by conversion processes involves breaking, rearranging, and/or recombining the starch chains. In some cases, the groupings normally present in the starch molecule may be transformed into other types, as for example, an hydroxyl group might be oxidized to an aldehyde, ketone, or carboxylic acid group. When conversion is carried out

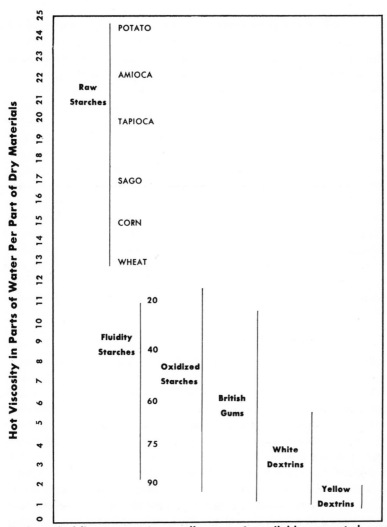

Each vertical line represents overall range of available converted products

FIGURE 2.6 Viscosity ranges for starch conversions. The comparative viscosity ranges of the various starches are shown in terms of parts of water to give roughly the same hot viscosity. This is an indication of the relative viscosities of the converted starches and their parent raw starches. Since a 20 fluidity starch is more viscous than a 75 fluidity starch, it can be seen that a 20 fluidity starch requires eleven parts of water to give about the same viscosity as a 75 fluidity starch with four parts of water. [*The Story of Starches*, 1953, National Starch Products, Inc. (now National Starch and Chemical Corporation).]

on a granule starch, the granule structure is weakened, so that the granules tend to fall apart to an extent determined by the type and degree of treatment. This, of course, results in a lower hot-paste viscosity and, in those products that do not retrograde on cooling (e.g., waxy starches), a lower cold-paste viscosity.

The conversion process may be effected through the action of enzymes, alkalies, acids, oxidizing agents, and/or heat. The last three are the agents usually employed in manufacturing the converted starches sold. Most of these commercial products are prepared by treatment of the starch granule either dry or in the form of an aqueous slurry. Conversions can be run on dispersed starch, such as is obtained by cooking in water, but these are made for special reasons. This type of conversion may be carried out at the point of application, as in the preparation of a paper-coating adhesive of proper viscosity by enzyme treatment. With more widespread use of continuous cookers, the use of acid for *in situ* conversion may also develop. In addition, conversion treatments of dispersed starch may also be employed in the manufacture of liquid adhesives sold in liquid form or drum-dried to yield cold water-soluble products.

Thin-Boiling Starches

Controlled acid hydrolysis yields thin-boiling or "fluidity" starches in a wide range of viscosities below that of the original starch. They are prepared by heating a slurry containing at least 35 per cent starch and a small amount of strong acid (0.2 to 2 per cent) at a temperature below the gelatinization temperature until the desired degree of conversion is obtained. At this point the reaction is stopped by neutralization and the product recovered by filtration and drying.

These products have high gel strengths and film-forming properties which are of interest in textile warp-sizing operations, and in gum candies. When an aqueous slurry is gelatinized by heating, the granules of an acid-converted starch do not swell to as great a volume as the unmodified starch but tend to disintegrate after limited swelling. This means that a lower peak viscosity is obtained in the initial cooking cycle and that the fluidity starch will disperse more rapidly to a clear, fluid sol. However, on cooling, these dispersions retrograde quickly, forming firm gels. This is particularly noticeable in the low- and intermediate-converted products.

The acid-converted waxy starches reflect the inherent sol stability of the raw starch, being more resistant to gelling. At high concentrations (45 to 50 per cent), however, the acid-converted waxy starches will also tend to gel. These waxy fluidity starches are useful where stable, low-viscosity, high-solids dispersions are required, such as in adhesive applications and paper surface sizing.

A fluidity-scale is used to describe the degree of treatment of these commercial products. The higher the fluidity, the more degraded the starch and therefore the less viscous the dispersion for a given concentration. The common fluidity starches range from 20 to 90 (see Figure 2.6).

The textile and paper industries use about 75 per cent of the annual consumption of acid-converted corn starch, with textile sizing and finishing taking more than half of this amount. The remainder is used in candy manufacture and in miscellaneous food, drug, and industrial applications.

Oxidized Starches

Commercial oxidations to prepare thin-boiling converted starches generally employ alkaline sodium hypochlorite, hence the term "chlorinated starch" even though no chloro-groups are introduced. These oxidized starches are available in about the same fluidity range as the acid-converted starches but give dispersions that are clearer and less congealing. Just as with acid conversions, the oxidations are run on aqueous slurries of the starch, stopping the reaction at the desired degree of conversion by destroying excess oxidant, acidifying, and recovering the granule product by filtration.

In addition to cutting the chain length, hypochlorite treatment also results in oxidation of hydroxyl groups to carbonyl and carboxyl groups. The presence of these bulky groups on the linear fraction of the starch disrupts the linearity of the molecular chains somewhat so that they cannot associate readily. Consequently, retrogradation is hindered and these products yield more stable dispersions (sols show less tendency to gel). The carboxyl groups also have a solubilizing action. These effects show up in the increasing clarity and decreasing gel strength as degree of oxidation increases. As with the acid-converted products, these oxidized starches have a weakened granule structure which results in a more rapid cooking product giving a lower peak viscosity.

The lower fluidity (40 to 50) oxidized starches are used in liquid laundry starches. The more highly oxidized starches are of particular interest in the paper industry for surface sizing and as a binder in clay coating where they are excellent dispersants for the clay and also yield high binding strength. The oxidized starches have an adverse effect on repulping the paper for reuse in that they tend to disperse clay and pigments making retention difficult in the newly formed sheet.

About 85 per cent of the annual consumption of oxidized corn starch in the United States is used in the manufacture of paper products. Textile finishing and laundry starches consume about one-third of the remainder with the rest being used primarily in building materials and binders.

Dextrinization

When dry starch is roasted either alone or in the presence of acid, British Gums or dextrins are produced by a number of degradation-recombination reactions. The properties obtained vary depending on the treatment, the products having generally low to intermediate viscosity, good stability against gelling, and partial to complete cold-water solubility.[1] Some combinations of these properties cannot be obtained by conversions run in aqueous starch slurries. Furthermore, the increased solubility makes it uneconomical to prepare this type of low-viscosity product by a wet conversion because of high losses of solubles during preparation. These products have been known for some time and have found a market primarily as adhesives or binders.

The dry conversion reactions are started and maintained by heat and are stopped by cooling or, in some cases, neutralization. The type and degree of reaction may be controlled by the use of acids, salts, buffers, and moisture which are sprayed on the commercially dry or low-moisture starch used as starting material. The extent of the conversion reaction is determined by the time-temperature relationships in the heating cycle. Although the changes involved are complex, three types of chemical transformations appear to predominate as shown in Figure 2.7:

(1) *Hydrolysis* of the linkages between glucose units catalyzed by acid and moisture to reduce the size of the molecules.

(2) *Rearrangement* of the molecules by breaking glucose-glucose linkage at one point in a chain and reforming it at another point to give increased branches.

(3) *Repolymerization* of small fragments to larger molecules by the catalytic action of high temperature and acid under anhydrous conditions.

The types of products obtained are determined by the extent to which these reactions take place. Three major types are sold: white dextrins, yellow dextrins, and British Gums. Dextrins are also formulated with borax and

---

[1] Although the size and state of aggregation of the dextrin molecules in dextrin-water systems generally places the mixture in the range considered for colloidal dispersions, it is common practice to refer to dextrin dispersions as solutions. The more highly converted dextrins will contain large quantities of material that are water-soluble in the usual sense.

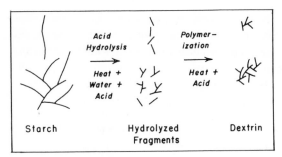

FIGURE 2.7 Hydrolysis and repolymerization during dextrinization of starch. (*Corn Starch*, 2d ed., 1958, Corn Industries Research Foundation, Inc., now Corn Refiners Association, Inc., Washington, D.C.)

sold as "borated dextrins." These are used in adhesives where their increased tackiness and water-absorption are useful.

About 40 per cent of the total annual U.S. consumption of dextrins is in adhesives, and somewhat less than this is used in paper and textile manufacture. The remainder is used in foundry core binders, building material binders, pharmaceuticals, and miscellaneous food and industrial applications.

White dextrins Since the preparation of white dextrins is carried out at relatively low temperature (generally below 300F) in the presence of moisture and high acidity (usually hydrochloric acid sprayed on the "dry" starch), it would be expected that hydrolytic breakdown would be the main reaction. The properties of white dextrins reflect this. Depending upon the degree of conversion, they range from a relatively high molecular weight to products with a degree of polymerization (DP) of 20 or less glucose units linked in the chain.

They tend to be light in color (white or off-white), have a low cold-water solubility (require cooking to disperse), and form aqueous dispersions which are unstable (the cooled solutions setting to soft pastes).

The white dextrins are formulated in adhesives (for uses such as envelope back-seams, paper bags). Library pastes are made with white dextrins as are some types of textile finishes.

Yellow dextrins These are made by heating starch at relatively high temperature (about 300 to 375F) with moderate acidity and low moisture (as compared to white dextrins). As the reaction proceeds, the initial hydrolysis gives way to rearrangement and repolymerization leading to highly branched molecules. As was pointed out previously, highly branched starches do not retrograde easily and hence dispersions of yellow dextrins have excellent stability.

The yellow dextrins are relatively low molecular weight polymers with a degree of polymerization in the approximate range of 20 to 50. They are the most highly converted of the treated starches and are essentially completely soluble in cold water and have a low viscosity. This means that it is possible to make concentrated (50 to 60 per cent) solutions which will remain relatively fluid. These solutions are very sticky or tacky and, because of the high solids, are fast drying. These properties are of value in adhesives applications which constitute the main use for yellow dextrins. They have been used on stamps, labels, envelopes.

British gums   In the conversions to make British Gums, starch of very low moisture and very little or no acidity is heated to high temperature (about 300 to 375F). These conditions favor rearrangement although some hydrolytic breakdown occurs in the initial stages of the reaction. As a result, British Gums are available in a wide range of viscosities, from close to that of the original starch down almost to that of yellow dextrins.

The high degree of branching makes for greater stability in dispersions and higher solubility compared to white dextrins. The color varies from light to dark brown. Aqueous dispersions of British Gums tend to have good spreadability (filminess) and gumminess which make them suitable for adhesives.

STARCH DERIVATIVES

Starch can be modified to change some property of the granule and/or molecule so that the starch will meet the requirements for specific uses more readily. In most cases, interest is centered on water-dispersible products. Since starch is inherently water-dispersible, it is not necessary to prepare highly substituted derivatives to impart solubility (as in the case of cellulose). Thus, relatively small numbers of substituent groupings can be employed to obtain the desired properties.

The degree of substitution (DS) involved is usually not more than one group per glucose unit, with the DS ranging in most commercial products at about one substituent per 20 to 50 glucose units. Highly substituted starch derivatives with a DS greater than one substituent per glucose unit are of little commercial importance at present, although these have been prepared in the laboratory or, in some cases, on a larger scale.

Low-substituted, water-dispersible derivatives are commercially available in large quantities and are generally in the 9 to 25 cents per pound price range with the major proportion in the neighborhood of 9 to 18 cents per pound.

By using converted starches as bases for derivatization treatments, a range of viscosity grades is available. Similarly, by using different varieties of starch, a range of properties characteristic of the specific varieties can be obtained in the derivatives.

Derivatization Processes

Some derivatization reactions are carried out on dry starch by blending in the reagents, effecting the reaction (generally by the application of heat or alkaline or acid conditions), and recovering the product directly in a dry form. This permits the economical preparation of cold-water-soluble starch derivatives without expensive product recovery procedures. Practically all starch products can be manufactured in a cold-water-dispersible form by precooking and drying on heated rolls or spray-drying. These pregelatinized products are attractive to users who cannot utilize cooking procedures or chemical techniques to disperse granular starches.

The cookable, granular starch derivatives are generally prepared in aqueous reactions in which a 40 to 45 per cent solids starch slurry is treated with the reagents, usually under alkaline conditions. Since the gelatinization temperature of starch is lowered as the number of derivatizing groups introduced is increased, there is a limit to the degree of substitution that can be reached by this method.

The swelling of higher DS derivatives (up to roughly one substituent to 10 glucose units) in the alkaline reaction mixture can be repressed to some extent by the addition of alkali metal salts, such as sodium sulfate and sodium chloride. Where the swelling cannot be controlled, it may be allowed to proceed and the product recovered by drying on heated rolls.

Stabilizing Modification

The tendency of starch dispersions to increase in viscosity and/or gel on cooling or aging has been a problem in many applications. As mentioned earlier, this is due to the tendency of the linear amylose molecules, present in most starches, to aggregate and become insoluble. This association tendency can be decreased or eliminated by the introduction of substituent groupings along the chain to interfere with the parallel alignment of linear chains. This is accomplished by esterifying or etherifying a few of the hydroxyl groups along the chain.

For example, dispersions of cornstarch acetates containing 1 to 4 per cent by weight acetyl groups are very much more stable than those of untreated cornstarch and can be used in textile and paper-sizing operations. Other derivatives, such as the hydroxyethyl ethers of cornstarch, are also stable and are useful in similar applications. As mentioned previously, starch from the waxy hybrid varieties of corn and sorghum contain little or no amylose and therefore yield stable dispersions. However, in some applications, such as in liquid laundry starches where instability may be promoted by repeated freezing and thawing during storage and shipment, the stability of these dispersions can be increased by using a modified waxy starch. For starches to be used in frozen foods, a modified waxy starch may also be necessary to withstand the effects of prolonged freezing.

Functional Groups

Starch ether and ester derivatives containing hydrophilic groups have markedly different properties than the raw starches. Derivatives containing carboxyl, sulfonate, or sulfate groups in the form of sodium or ammonium salts have a very high affinity for water which results in high-viscosity, clear, non-gelling dispersions. The dried films of these products are easily redissolved, making them of particular value in textile sizing and printing where ease of removal from fabrics is of importance.

The presence of anionic groups such as sulfate, sulfonate, or phosphate and cationic groups such as amino groups is reflected in the properties of the dispersions and their behavior at various pH levels. These charged substituents have a marked effect on the bonding of starch to various substrates, and thereby can aid in the more efficient utilization of basic starch properties in adhesive and sizing operations. For example, a starch derivative containing tertiary amino groups has a strong positive charge and is attracted and held by cellulose products which generally have a negative charge. Thus, in the wet-end sizing of paper, the cationic starch is generally more effective than native starch since it is more efficiently retained in the wet paper web and has strength-improving properties beyond those of ordinary raw starch.

The introduction of hydrophobic groups, such as long aliphatic hydrocarbon chains, results in a water-repellent starch. This type of starch derivative can be dispersed in water under special conditions but will dry to a water-repellent film. Derivatives containing long-chain hydrophobic groups are of potential interest where emulsifying and protective colloidal action is needed.

Miscellaneous Derivatives

A large number of derivatives has been prepared and many have been offered for sale or used commercially. Starch nitrate, a high D.S. derivative, is manufactured by the Trojan Powder Company, Allentown, Pa., for use in blasting explosives. Allyl starch, another highly substituted derivative, was offered as a solvent-soluble, curable starch for use in applications such as protective finishes for wood or a printing ink component. This is not currently on the market. In 1966, Eastman Chemical Products, Inc., Kingsport, Tennessee, offered a high D.S. cyanoethyl starch at $30 per pound. This product is reported to have a high dielectric constant suggesting potential use in electroluminescent components.

The list of derivatives prepared is a long one, representative types including alkyl, carboxymethyl, sulfoethyl, cyanoethyl, aminoethyl, amidoethyl, quaternary ammonium alkyl, and hydroxyalkyl ethers as well as sulfate, phosphate, acrylate, fatty acid, maleate, succinate, phthalate and benzoate esters. A unique hydrophobic ester derivative having remarkable dry powder fluid flow properties is marketed under the tradename Dry-Flo[1] for use as a dusting powder and lubricating agent. Carboxymethyl starch is a cold-water-dispersible product marketed commercially as the sodium salt. Starch sulfate is also available in semi-commercial quantities.

Several derivatives which are sold in carload quantities deserve special mention. These are starch acetate, hydroxyethyl starch ether, and cationic aminoalkyl ethers. Other derivatives which have stimulated a great deal of development work are the phosphate starches and periodate oxystarches.

Starch acetates These can be prepared by treatment of aqueous suspensions of starch with acetic anhydride[2] or vinyl acetate.[3] The commercial products are low-substituted cornstarch esters containing less than 0.2 acetyl groups per anhydroglucose unit. They are sold under tradenames such as Kofilm[4] and Mirafilm.[5] They are available in a range of viscosities and cook to noncongealing sols. These products have good hydrating capacity, flow, filming, and viscosity stability in their sols and give clear, flexible, water-soluble, non-tacky films. They generally have a slightly lower gelatinization temperature than cornstarch.

These products can be used to apply oil- and grease-resistant films to paper. Addition of thermosetting resins or other insolubilizing chemicals will render the films water-resistant. These starch esters are compatible over wide concentration limits with a variety of clays, pigments, and other hydrophilic materials such as polyvinyl alcohol, water-soluble cellulose derivatives, algins, proteins; and many other water-soluble natural and synthetic film-formers.

These products are used primarily in textile and paper applications where they are useful in sizing and coating. The starch acetates are also useful for

[1] Product of National Starch and Chemical Corporation.
[2] U.S. Patent 2,461,139 (1949).
[3] U.S. Patent 2,928,828 (1960).
[4] Product of National Starch and Chemical Corporation.
[5] Product of A. E. Staley Manufacturing Company.

commercial laundry starches and as suspending and thickening agents. Special grades of acetates are also used in processed foods for thickening and stabilizing. These products are made from corn, waxy corn, and tapioca starches. They may contain up to 2.5 per cent acetyl groups, meeting the requirements for "Food Starch-Modified" under Food Additives Regulation 121.1031.[1] Products of this type are sold under tradenames such as ColFlo[2] and Mira-Cleer.[3]

Hydroxyethyl ethers   These are low-substituted hydroxyethyl cornstarch ethers (DS 0.05 to 0.10 hydroxyethyl groups per anhydroglucose unit) which are marketed under such tradenames as Penford Gum,[4] Essex Gum,[4] EOsize,[5] Supersize,[6] Superflex,[6] ClinEO,[7] and Amaizo 700[8] starches. They are prepared by treating starch with ethylene oxide.[9] These products have properties similar to the acetates and compete with them. They too cook to noncongealing sols which dry to clear, flexible, hydrophilic, nontacky, remoistenable films. The hydroxyethyl groups are attached to the starch by ether linkages which resist cleavage by acid, alkaline, or mild oxidizing agents. They are compatible with a variety of water-soluble filmformers, reactive with insolubilizing agents, etc. The hydroxyethyl ethers are used in textile sizing and finishing as well as in paper sizing and coating and in various adhesive applications.

Mention should be made that hydroxypropyl starch ethers can be prepared by treatment with propylene oxide. These products have properties similar to the hydroxyethyl ethers. However, the hydroxypropyl ethers may be used in foods under Food Additives Regulation 121.1031,[10] whereas the hydroxyethyl ethers are not cleared for food use. Products for food use, particularly in food subjected to low-temperature storage, are under development and are available in commercial quantities. Hydroxypropylation of high amylose starch resulted in an increase in the elongation and bursting strength of films prepared from these starches.[11]

Amine starches   These products are generally low-substituted ether or ester derivatives (D.S. about 0.05 or less) containing tertiary amine or quaternary ammonium groups which impart a cationic charge to the

[1] Code of Federal Regulations, Title 21.
[2] Product of National Starch and Chemical Corporation.
[3] Product of A. E. Staley Manufacturing Company.
[4] Product of Penick and Ford, Ltd., Inc.
[5] Product of Corn Products Company.
[6] Product of Stein, Hall, and Company, Inc.
[7] Product of Clinton Corn Processing Company, Division of Standard Brands Inc.
[8] Product of American Maize-Products Company.
[9] U.S. Patents 2,516,632–3–4 (1950).
[10] Code of Federal Regulations, Title 21.
[11] W. B. Roth and C. L. Mehltretter, Food Technology, **21**, 72–74 (1967).

starch.[1] The cationic charge causes these starches to be substantive to cellulosic materials, a property of value in paper and textile applications. They are also effective flocculants in many systems. Cationic starches which meet the Food Additives Regulations 121.2506 for "Industrial Starch-Modified"[2] (used as components of food-packaging materials) are prepared by treatment of starch with (4-chlorobutene-2) - trimethylammonium chloride, β-diethylaminoethylchloride hydrochloride, dimethylaminoethyl-methacrylate, and 2,3-epoxypropyltrimethylammonium chloride.

The commercial development of these cationic starches was initiated in 1955 by the National Starch and Chemical Corporation with the sale of products for use as paper additives at the wet-end of the paper-making process. At present, a number of cationic corn and potato starch products are available in commercial quantities from several manufacturers. These products are sold under tradenames such as Astro X-100,[3] Cato,[4] Electra,[5] Q-Tac,[6] Sta-Lok,[7] and Supercharg.[8]

As with most starches, the cationic starches are available in a number of viscosity grades and as pregelatinized, cold-water-dispersible products.

Phosphate starches These are cookable, granular low-sub-stituted monophosphate esters (DS 0.05 or less) or cold-water-dispersible, higher substituted monophosphates (DS greater than 0.07). They are generally prepared by impregnating starch with the sodium acid salts of ortho-, pyro-, or tripolyphosphoric acid, drying the mixture to 5 to 10 per cent moisture, and heating at 240 to 340F for a short time (1 to 3 hours).[9] These products differ from the cross-linked, inhibited granule phosphates which are mixtures of mono-, di-, and triesters, formed by treatment of starch with phosphorus oxychloride or sodium trimetaphosphate mentioned in the section on "Modification by Cross-Linking."

The properties of the starch monophosphate esters will vary depending upon D.S., pH and temperature of phosphation, type of starch, and presence of cross-linking. Generally the products will tend to have greater clarity, less tendency to gel on cooling, and higher viscosity than the untreated starch base. The pastes in water tend to have long, cohesive flow char-acteristics. The viscosity of aqueous dispersions of starch phosphates is markedly decreased by salts.

[1] U.S. Patents 2,813,093 (1957); 2,876,217 (1959); 3,336,292 (1967); 3,346,563 (1967).
[2] Code of Federal Regulations, Title 21, Subpart F, Section 121.2506.
[3] Products of Penick and Ford, Ltd.
[4] Products of National Starch and Chemical Corporation.
[5] Products of Anheuser-Busch, Inc.
[6] Products of Corn Products Company.
[7] Products of A. E. Staley Manufacturing Company.
[8] Products of Stein-Hall and Company, Inc.
[9] U.S. Patents 2,865,762 (1958); 2,884,412–3 (1958); 2,961,440 (1960).

Uses for these products have been suggested in thickening foods,[1] as fillers and binders in pharmaceuticals, as flocculants in ore refining, as foundry core binders, and as a depressant in ore flotation. The Corn Products Company offers a cross-bonded, waxy milo phosphate starch for use in foods. The American Maize-Products Company has offered a line of starch phosphates of varying phosphate content, viscosity, and purity.

Dialdehyde starch[2]   This starch derivative is prepared by treating starch with periodic acid to selectively oxidize the hydroxyl groups on carbon atoms two and three to aldehyde groups as shown in Figure 2.8.

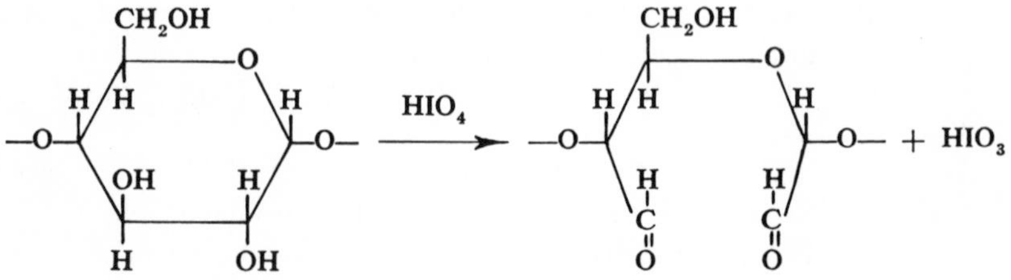

Glucose unit in starch   *Dialdehyde unit in oxystarch*

FIGURE 2.8   The periodate oxidation reaction of starch.

All degrees of oxidation, up to 100 per cent, of the glucose units in the starch molecule can be obtained. Since periodic acid is an expensive reagent, the process is commercially feasible only because the periodic acid can be regenerated electrolytically from by-product iodate.

This process was first developed by W. Dvonch and C. L. Mehltretter of the Northern Utilization Research and Development Division, U.S. Department of Agriculture.[3] The commercialization of this process was achieved by the Chemicals Division of Miles Laboratories, Inc., Elkhart, Indiana, which is offering dialdehyde starch on a commercial scale under the tradename Sumstar. A developmental price of 75 cents per pound has been set (1967) with the prospect of a 35 to 40 cents per pound price predicted for multimillion pound production levels.

Although the dialdehyde starch is generally represented with free aldehyde groups as in Figure 2.8, the available evidence indicates these groups are present as various hydrated forms including inter- and intra-molecular

[1] As specified in Federal Food & Drug Regulations, 121.1031 (op. cit.), products classified as "Food Starch-Modified" are prepared with sodium tripolyphosphate and trimetaphosphate and may not contain more than 0.4 per cent phosphorus.

[2] C. L. Mehltretter, *Staerke*, **18**, #7,208–213 (1966) reviews "Recent Progress in Dialdehyde Starch Technology."

[3] V. F. Pfeiffer, *et al.*, *Ind. Eng. Chem.*, **52**, 201–206 (1960); U.S. Patent 2,648,629.

hemiacetals. The presence of aldehyde groups in dialdehyde starch suggests reactivity with a number of reagents such as alcohols to form acetals, sodium bisulfite to form aldehyde-addition products, ammonia and amines to form nitrogen-containing adducts, etc. The aldehyde groups can be oxidized further with chlorous acid to yield a polycarboxylate polymer, possibly of interest as a thickener. The dialdehyde starch can be treated with reducing agents such as sodium borohydride to yield the corresponding polyalcohol. Hydrolysis of the dialdehyde starch (100 per cent oxidized) with concentrated sulfurous acid will yield glyoxal and the sugar, D-erythrose. Hydrogenolysis under high pressure in the presence of catalysts will yield erythritol, a polyhydroxy-compound. Thus, the dialdehyde starch is the potential source of new types of polymeric materials and of various low molecular weight organic chemicals.

The dialdehyde starches are insoluble in cold water and swell on heating to 90 to 95C. The more highly oxidized the starch, the more difficult it is to disperse by cooking in water. At high levels of oxidation, the starch granules swell to some extent on cooking in water at 90C and this swelling causes gelation at concentrations in the range of 10 per cent. On heating in water for prolonged periods, the products lose viscosity and tend to develop a tan to brown color, presumably due to degradation of the polymer.

The aqueous suspensions initially at a pH of approximately 5.5 to 6 tend to become acid (about pH 3 to 4) on heating. Sumstar dialdehyde starches are described as dispersible on heating at 90 to 100C for 30 to 60 minutes in water of about 100 ppm alkalinity as calcium carbonate. Under these conditions, controlled depolymerization occurs and dispersions of optimum molecular weight are obtained. Strongly alkaline conditions cause rapid and excessive depolymerization of dialdehyde starch with color formation and the production of acidic groups.

Current development work has indicated potential application areas for dialdehyde starch in paper, adhesives, leather tanning, and homogenized tobacco sheets. These applications are based primarily on the ability of the aldehyde groups to cross-link hydroxyl-, amino-, or imino-containing polymers. Studies indicate that highly oxidized dialdehyde starch is valuable for tanning light-colored garment leathers and as a pretannage for the rapid vegetable tanning of sole leathers.

The more highly oxidized dialdehyde starches (90 to 100 per cent) appear to be excellent surface sizes, imparting wet- and dry-strength with a low dispersion viscosity. Good wet strength is obtainable by wet-end addition of the dialdehyde starch in conjunction with a cationic retention agent. This is of particular interest in the production of wet-strength paper toweling and tissue. Further work is in progress on its use in paper coatings. In general, the dialdehyde starches may be of value where an easily handled, odorless, aldehyde-type cross-linking or hardening agent is required.

COMMERCIAL USAGE

Sales of cornstarch and its modifications in the United States amounted to roughly 2.74 billion pounds in 1965 and 2.85 billion pounds in 1966. Approximately 50 per cent was consumed by the paper and paper products industry. Starch consumption by the textile industry in 1965 and 1966 comprised roughly 14 per cent of total cornstarch sales. The use of starch in foods, mainly processed foods, amounted to about 15 per cent of annual cornstarch sales. The remaining 21 per cent was used in various industrial and governmental applications such as pharmaceuticals, mining, adhesives, building materials, explosives.

Foods

Starches are used in the preparation of beer, baking powder, bakery products, pie fillings, pudding mixes, salad dressings, canned foods, frozen foods, dry food mixes, confections, and snack foods.

Although starch is the primary carbohydrate energy source in the human diet, the use of starch in food products is based mainly on its ability to make foods more appealing to the eye and palate. This is particularly important in the United States where the preparation, transportation, and storage of food products have reached a high degree of technical sophistication which supplies the consumer with an abundance and variety of foods without regard to season or distance. This has also led to high consumer demand for the so-called "convenience foods" which require a minimum of preparation in the home, restaurant, or cafeteria kitchen while still providing high quality in nutritional value, taste, and eye appeal. Thus, the starches used in preparing food products must meet exacting requirements during all phases of the preparation, storage, transportation, and final cooking of the food.

Starches are used in foods as a bland carrier for flavor and to provide appropriate viscosity properties, texture or "mouth-feel," clarity, and stability. These objectives are attained by manipulation of the inherent properties of starch described previously: its gelatinization and water-holding or thickening power, variable gelling or non-gelling properties, binding and adhesive characteristics, film-forming ability, and emulsion-stabilization properties. Thus, by the choice of the type starch (corn, waxy corn, tapioca, etc.) and the modification (conversion, cross-linking, derivatization), a starch product can be prepared to meet the requirements for a particular type of food product. For example, by a judicious combination of cross-linking (e.g., phosphate, epichlorohydrin) and derivatization (acetate, phosphate, hydroxypropyl ether) of a tapioca, waxy corn, or waxy sorghum starch, a thickener for fruit pie fillings or toppings can be made. This starch thickener resists viscosity breakdown during cooking in contact with the fruit acids, gives good clarity and sheen to bring out the fresh fruit appearance, has a bland flavor that does not mask the fruit flavor, and is resistant to over-cooking so that the juices do not boil out of the pie during baking. In addition, the starch gives a heavy, short, smooth, non-rubbery texture with a pleasant "mouth-feel." The starch thickener does not set to an opaque, rigid gel and thereby retains the smooth texture and clarity. It is thick enough, however, so that the filling does not flow out when the pie is cut. Further, when the pie or pie-filling is stored at room temperature or lower (down to 0F), the texture remains the same and there is no syneresis or "weeping" of the liquid contents from the filling. Products of this type are marketed under various tradenames such as ColFlo67,[1] Fruit-Fill,[2] F.T.D. Food Starch-Modified #4832,[3] Mira-Cleer,[4] and Polar-Gel.[5]

Starches may be used as processing aids to maintain solids in suspension, to give proper filling viscosity, and prevent splashing during high-speed container-filling operations. By maintaining a low viscosity of the thickener during retort sterilization of cans, better heat penetration can be obtained and hence a shorter exposure time to high temperature with resultant improved flavor. Low-moisture starches may be used to absorb moisture to insure flowability of powders and dehydrated foods in container-filling and when the consumer pours the product from the container. In all cases, the starch must be designed to withstand the rigors of the processing conditions (high shear, high temperature, low pH) so that it can perform its function in the final product. Sometimes, modified starches are added to foods to restore the natural texture which may have been smeared out by the processing (e.g. to restore pulpy appearance of dehydrated foods, tomato sauces, vegetable soups, fruit fillings, and drinks).

Modified starches have also been used as binders in various types of extruded foods such as snacks and potato products. Modified high amylose starches have found use in coatings on French-fried potatoes to inhibit fat-pickup and to control fat penetration and browning. Dextrins have been useful in encapsulation of beverage clouding agents and flavors, in emulsion stabilization, in dispersions of fats in butter-sauces, and in coating and glazing of bakery products and confections.

The Federal Food and Drug Administration, under the Federal Food, Drug, and Cosmetic Act and the Food Additives Amendment to it, regulates

[1] Product of National Starch and Chemical Corporation.
[2] Product of Morningstar-Paisley, Incorporated.
[3] Product of Corn Products Company.
[4] Product of A. E. Staley Manufacturing Company.
[5] Product of American Maize-Products Company.

the use of starch products as foods. Unmodified starches, dextrins, and many converted starches or modified starches are either "generally recognized as safe" for use in foods or have been cleared for use under Food Additives Regulation 121.1031, "Food Starch-modified." Other modified starches would require similar clearance before they could be used in foods.

Paper Industry

The paper and paper products industry is the largest industrial consumer of starch products, with an annual consumption of corn starch close to 1.5 billion pounds in 1966. About 35 per cent of this volume consisted of modified starches and starch derivatives. Starch products are used as wet-end additives, as surface sizes, as binders in clay and pigment coatings, and in adhesives required in the manufacture of paper products.

Wet-end additives are added to the pulp prior to the formation of the paper to improve the strength and sheet properties of the paper. A considerable quantity of modified starches and starch derivatives as well as raw starches are used. These are generally added in the range of 0.2 to 3 per cent by weight of the fiber, the higher range being used for heavier weight paper and board. A starch derivative with a low gelatinization temperature (e.g., starch hydroxyethyl ether) may be added here in granule form, and that portion held in the wet paper web will gelatinize when the sheet is passed over the dryers, thereby increasing internal fiber bonding.

The cationic amine starch derivatives described previously have found wide acceptance as wet-end additives at addition levels of 0.2 to 1.0 per cent by weight of the pulp. These products have a positive charge and are therefore strongly attracted to the negatively charged cellulose fibers. This results in practically complete retention of the starch in the fast-moving paper web formed on the paper machine wire. No other starch is retained in the paper as well as this. Consequently, all the cationic starch added in the beater or headbox is held in close attachment to the fibers in the paper web where it will be of most value for interfiber bonding.

This type of product is very effective in increasing the tensile and bursting strength of the paper. Because of its interaction with inert fillers such as clays, carbonates, and titanium dioxide, it is also an effective pigment-retention aid. It is unusual in this respect in that it improves pigment retention while retaining a high proportion of the strength of the sheet. The cationic starch holds tenaciously to the paper and is not removed under the usual conditions found in food packaging.

After the paper is formed it may be given a sizing treatment to improve strength and surface properties, such as printability, grease resistance, gloss, scuff-resistance, etc. Here, controlled viscosity and viscosity stability of the sizing solution are important as are film properties. Some special starches for enzyme conversion and oxidized starches are employed as well as stable derivatives such as acetates and hydroxyethyl ethers selling at 8 to 10 cents per pound. This operation is the largest consumer of starches in the paper field and is expanding. A recent development is the use of continuous high-temperature cookers to reduce the viscosity of unmodified or slightly modified (acid, oxidation) starches for size press application. Here the reduction in viscosity is effected by the high temperature and shearing forces in the cooker, sometimes aided by the presence of chemical reagents which have a degrading action on starch (acids, acid salts, oxidizing agents).

Paper coatings are applied to improve the printing surface and color, add weight, or impart special characteristics. For high-speed coating, required properties for the binder are high binding strength and suitable rheological characteristics (controlled viscosity, good flow, viscosity stability, and good water-holding properties to minimize penetration into the stock). Oxidized starches, dextrins, and enzyme-converted starches, as well as derivatives such as hydroxyethyl starch ethers or starch acetates, are used as the binder in the pigment coating. Water-resistant, starch-bound coatings are prepared through the use of combinations of starch with insolubilizing resins, such as urea-formaldehyde. Recently, cationic starch has shown some advantages as a paper coating binder over the usual starches. They appear to be more effective binders and are useable at reduced levels, giving better opacity and gloss. Further, they have shown wet-rub resistance equivalent to casein, when treated with insolubilizers such as glyoxal.[1]

Modified starches are also being used in various converting operations such as corrugating, laminating, bag making, etc. The waxy starches are used in gummed tapes where animal glue was formerly the exclusive remoistening adhesive. Here, gloss, remoistenability, and quick tack are required.

Textile Industry

Starch has been used in the textile industry in sizing warp yarns, finishing, and printing fabrics. It has been estimated that the annual consumption of starch by the textile mills averaged about 375 million pounds during 1960–1964.[2] This consisted of roughly 345 million pounds of corn and sorghum starch including dextrins, about 10 to 12 million pounds of wheat starch,

---

[1] E. D. Mazzarella and L. J. Hickey, *TAPPI*, **49**, 526–532 (1966).
[2] "An Economic Evaluation of Starch Use in the Textile Industry," U.S. Dept. of Agriculture, Economic Research Service, Agricultural Economic Report No. 109, Washington, D.C., March, 1967, p. 8.

and very roughly 20 million pounds of potato starch and 5 million pounds of tapioca starch. According to the estimate, at least 80 per cent of this starch was used for warp sizing with the major part of the remainder used in finishing. The shipments of grain and sorghum starches and dextrins to the Textile Industry in the 1964–1966 period averaged about 365 million pounds per year.

In the warp-sizing or "slashing" operation, the yarn is passed through an aqueous solution of a polymer such as starch to apply a protective coating (probably discontinuous). This is necessary to enable the yarn to withstand the abrasive action encountered in the weaving process, thereby minimizing breaks and shedding which result in costly reductions in weaving efficiency and defects in the fabric. The slashing process requires material which can be dispersed easily to give viscosity-stable, non-congealing, non-foaming size solutions that deposit tough, flexible, non-tacky, strongly adhering, non-shedding films on the yarn. The film must be relatively insensitive to overdrying and high humidity. The film should also be easily solubilized and removed by the enzyme treatment and/or washing of the desizing operation.

Three types of yarns are sized: spun yarns of natural fibers, spun yarns of synthetic fibers, and continuous-filament yarns. The natural fiber yarns are hydrophilic while the synthetics (except viscose rayon) are hydrophobic. Starch generally performs well on hydrophilic fibers but requires modification to perform on hydrophobic fibers where there is difficulty in obtaining penetration and adhesion. Starch or modified starches are used in sizing cellulosic yarns, spun synthetic fiber, or staple yarns, and blends of natural and synthetic fibers. It is not used to any extent for sizing synthetic filament yarns where synthetic polymers have been more effective. Starches are used for sizing because they do the job at lower cost than the synthetic resins such as polyvinyl alcohol or polyacrylic acid.

In warp sizing, the acid-converted fluidity starches are used because they are inexpensive although they do not have the non-congealing character that is desired. Oxidized starches, hydroxyethyl starch ethers, starch acetates, and other esters are used depending upon the type of yarn (cotton, wool, rayon, etc.) and the requirements of the specific mill operation. The high amylose corn starches and their derivatives are becoming important because of their increased film strength. The high amylose types are also being used for sizing glass fibers. To improve the removal of the starch size from the fabric before finishing, the presence of hydrophilic groups such as sulfonate, sulfate, or carboxylate is of value.

Textile finishes are applied to impart or enhance the desirable properties of the fabrics such as crease-resistance, shrink-resistance, softness, hand, draping properties, etc. Starches are used alone or in conjunction with thermosetting resins (e.g., urea- or melamine-formaldehyde) for finishing. Starch was originally used as a stiffening agent and both unmodified and modified starches are suitable for this. However, where other properties in addition to or in place of stiffness are required, the modified starches are used because of the viscosity-stability and non-congealing character of their dispersions. In addition, derivatized starches provide film clarity, which contributes to the brightness and sparkle of colored fabrics, and film flexibility which insures smoothness to the touch. The starch acetates and hydroxyethyl ethers as well as oxidized starches and dextrins are used in finishing formulations. However, it should be noted that starches alone are not sufficient to impart many of the properties that are required in finishing today such as water-proofing, fire-proofing, wash-and-wear, durable press. Hence, the market for starch in much of the finishing is giving way to synthetic materials. It is still used to a major extent in most work clothing and white goods.

The textile printing process for the reproduction of colored patterns on cloth requires thickeners for the dyes used. The dye pastes are carefully formulated to provide good dispersion of the expensive dyestuff, controlled transfer of the design to the cloth, and good color value. Modified starches, such as dextrins, carboxymethyl-, and hydroxyethyl-starch ethers have been used alone or in conjunction with other thickeners for this purpose. It should be pointed out, however, that the use of resin binders with water-insoluble pigments in place of the water-dispersible dyes has largely replaced the printing paste systems using starch and natural gum thickeners. These new systems are based primarily on a thickened water-in-oil emulsion.

Textile mill operations, where large quantities of desizing wastes are discharged into streams, must comply with state antipollution laws controlling such wastes. The primary measurement of the effect of these organic wastes on stream pollution is the biochemical oxygen demand (B.O.D.). The B.O.D. is the amount of oxygen that is removed from the water for bacterial decomposition of the organic waste and hence is not available to support life in the stream. B.O.D. is generally reported as parts (of oxygen) per million (of waste) or parts per hundred in terms of per cent.

One of the factors involved in the competition between starch and synthetic polymers in warp sizing is the relative B.O.D. of these materials because the desizing wastes are believed to affect significantly the B.O.D. of textile mill wastes.[1] The standard test now in use to determine the relative oxygen depletion expected in streams is a 5-day test whereby the B.O.D. of a given material is determined after 5 days of exposure to a test solution containing microorganisms that have been acclimated to the substrate to be

[1] Agricultural Economic Report #109, pp. 20–24.

tested. Of course, this time is arbitrary, since materials may decompose at different rates depending upon their susceptibility to microbiological attack. Ultimately, most organic materials will decompose and will require a definite amount of oxygen to be available for complete oxidation of each carbon and hydrogen atom in the compound, forming carbon dioxide and water (theoretical B.O.D.). Thus, the 5-day B.O.D. test measures only a fraction of the theoretical B.O.D. and there is insufficient data relating the 5-day test values to the pollution effects to be found under various conditions in streams.

In general, starches give relatively high values (50 to 85 per cent) in the 5-day B.O.D. test unless they are derivatized to a relatively high D.S. (0.5–2.0). Derivatives containing carboxymethyl, hydroxyethyl, cyanoethyl, and diethylaminoethyl groups have shown low 5-day B.O.D. test values (4–30 per cent) because they are more resistant to bacterial decomposition. In general, the higher the degree of substitution the lower the 5-day B.O.D. value for a given type of derivative. Some derivatizing groups are more effective than others in lowering the 5-day B.O.D. Sodium carboxymethylcellulose (CMC) and polyvinyl alcohol are representative of synthetic materials which give low 5-day B.O.D. values and have been used in textile sizing operations in place of starch. It is interesting that the theoretical B.O.D. of CMC is close to that of starch.

It should be noted that public concern over stream pollution is increasing. This is likely to result in ever more stringent laws concerning the dumping of wastes into streams. The most realistic approach to minimizing stream pollution is to minimize or eliminate the dumping of wastes into the streams. It is our opinion that waste-treatment plants which will remove or oxidize wastes before mill effluent is discharged into streams will eventually be required by law. Where waste-treatment plants are installed, materials that are readily biodegradable will have an advantage in terms of cost and time required for treatment. As mentioned above, starches are much more readily degradable than most synthetic polymers. There is some evidence to show that it is less costly to treat starch desizing wastes to lower B.O.D. than to use the higher priced synthetic materials on the assumption that no waste treatment will be required.[1] Furthermore, the product that can act as an effective size at a low level of deposition on the yarn ("add-on") will yield a smaller quantity of desizing waste for treatment. With the advent of high amylose starches, modifications of starch effective at lower add-on levels than conventional starches have been developed. An example of this type is a cationic starch sold under the tradename, Hi-Bond.[2]

[1] Agricultural Economic Report #109, pp. 24–27.
[2] Product of the National Starch & Chemical Corporation.

Miscellaneous

There are many other fields where modified starches may give improved performance. These areas include oil well drilling muds, flocculants, pharmaceuticals (thickeners, tablet disintegrants), packaging adhesives, explosives, ceramics, building materials (acoustical tile binders), foundry cores, etc. Space does not permit detailed discussion of these uses. It is suggested that starch suppliers be contacted for information on specific starch modifications or applications.

Many starch modifications can be made, as was indicated, but may not be offered for sale because a market is not known. Consequently, manufacturers of modified starches are usually interested in following up any inquiries indicating potential markets for experimental modifications as well as for standard starch modifications. In many cases, where the market potential warrants it, special modifications will be developed on request.

K. G. Scheffel

Technical Service and Development
The Dow Chemical Company
Midland, Michigan

3

Methyl- and Hydroxypropyl Methyl-Cellulose Derivatives

This chapter surveys some of the properties and uses of the methylcellulose and hydroxypropyl methylcellulose derivatives. Chemically, these products are cellulose ethers in which methyl or hydroxypropyl groups have been substituted upon one or more of the three hydroxyl groups present in each anhydroglucose ring of cellulose.

A typical basic structure may be represented by:

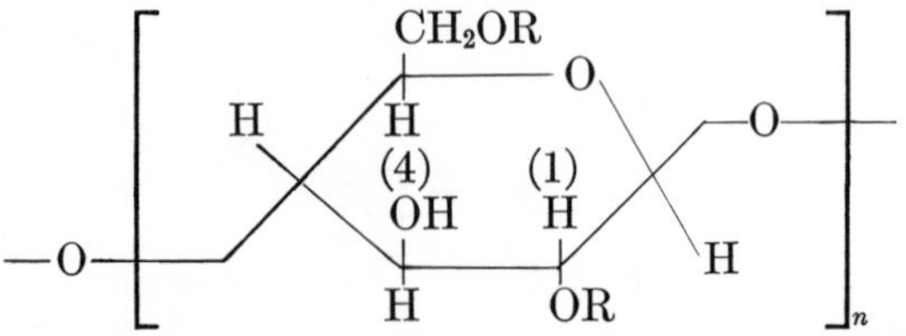

with R representing the methyl or hydroxypropyl substitution.

The number and distribution of the substituents required to achieve a given set of properties will vary with a specific substituent used. The effect of etherification is to disorder and spread apart the cellulose chains so water or other solvents may enter to effect solvation. By controlling the amount and type of substitution, it is possible to produce a range of widely varying properties. By varying the methoxyl or hydroxypropoxyl content, a series of polymers is produced which ranges from alkali soluble to organic soluble. The water soluble commercial derivatives contain approximately two substituted groups per anhydroglucose ring, while the organic soluble polymers approach almost total substitution, i.e., three groups per anhydroglucose unit.

THE MANUFACTURING PROCESS

The basic reactions required for the manufacture of methylcellulose are:

$$R\text{—}OH \quad + \quad NaOH \quad \rightarrow \quad R\text{—}ONa \quad + \quad H_2O$$

Cellulose   Sodium hydroxide   Alkali cellulose   Water

$$R\text{—}ONa \quad + \quad CH_3Cl \quad \rightarrow \quad R\text{—}OCH_3 \quad + \quad NaCl$$

Alkali cellulose   Alkyl halide   Methylcellulose   Sodium chloride

$$R\text{—}ONa \quad + \quad \overset{\displaystyle O}{\overset{\displaystyle /\backslash}{CH_2\text{—}CH_2}} \quad \rightarrow \quad ROCH_2CH_2OH$$

Alkali cellulose   Alkylene oxide   Hydroxyethylcellulose

If in addition to methyl chloride the alkali cellulose is reacted with propylene oxide, the mixed ether hydroxypropyl methylcellulose is produced.

Since the viscosity of the cellulose ether is related to the polymer molecular weight, control of the air oxidation of alkali cellulose (depolymerization) offers a means of producing cellulose ethers in a wide range of viscosities. The viscosity ranges for the commercially available methyl and hydroxypropyl methylcellulose ethers are shown in Table 3.1.

TABLE 3.1. Viscosities of Methocel®[1] Methylcellulose and Methocel Hydroxypropyl Methylcellulose.

Product	Nominal Viscosity[2] (cps)	Range[2] (cps)
Methocel MC methylcellulose	10	8– 12
	15	13– 18
	25	20– 30
	100	80– 120
	400	350– 550
	1,500	1,200– 1,800
	4,000	3,500– 5,600
	8,000	7,000–10,000
Methocel BL methylcellulose	250	200– 350
Methocel 60 HG hydroxypropyl methylcellulose	50	40– 60
	4,000	3,500– 5,600
Methocel 65 HG hydroxypropyl methylcellulose	50	40– 60
	400	350– 550
	1,500	1,200– 1,800
	4,000	3,500– 5,600
Methocel 90 HG hydroxypropyl methylcellulose	100	80– 120
	4,000	3,500– 5,600
	15,000	12,000–18,000
	50,000	40,000–60,000
Methocel HB hydroxybutyl methylcellulose	15,000	12,000–18,000

[1] Methocel is the registered trademark for the methylcellulose products manufactured by Dow Chemical Co.
[2] ASTM D1347–64.

PHYSICAL PROPERTIES

The physical properties of the Methocel cellulose ethers are summarized in Table 3.2.

TABLE 3.2.   Physical Properties of Methocel.

Color:	
Methocel	White
Apparent density; lb/cu ft	
Methocel MC, 4000 cps	18.1–25.6
Methocel MC, 400 cps	22.4–28.7
Methocel MC, 15 cps	26.2–31.2
Charring temperature, C(F)	
Methocel MC	300–305 (572–581F)
Methocel 65 HG	295–300 (554–572F)
Particle size:	
Methocel, % through 40 mesh	95
Moisture, as packed, %	
Methocel	3 max.

Solution Properties

Solutions of Methocel are non-Newtonian, i.e., the shearing stress applied is not directly proportional to the rate of shear. However, low-viscosity solutions very closely approach Newtonian flow, whereas high-viscosity solutions exhibit considerable pseudoplasticity. Figure 3.1 describes the typical behavior of solutions of Methocel MC of high, intermediate, and low viscosity.

The viscosities of the Methocel cellulose ethers are defined by the ASTM method D1347–64 and D2363–65T, in aqueous solutions, 2 per cent weight/weight concentrations at 20C. Figure 3.2 shows the typical viscosity-concentration relationships for Methocel cellulose ethers in water.

Thermal Gelation in Aqueous Solutions

The water-soluble Methocel cellulose ethers display the unique property of thermal gelation. That is, they gel on heating while many other natural gums, such as agar, gel on cooling. The probable explanation of this gelation phenomenon lies in the nature of the solution.

Methylcellulose exists in solution as an aggregate of long colloidal molecules hydrated by successive layers of water molecules which swell the bulk of the aggregate. These water molecules lubricate the chains and render the solution a smooth-pouring, viscous liquid.

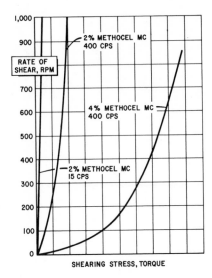

FIGURE 3.1   Rheograms of water-soluble methylcellulose resins in low-, intermediate- and high-viscosity solutions.

Upon application of heat, the energy of the loosely-bound water molecules increases and the outermost layers break away. When a sufficient number of water molecules are thermally disoriented, their lubricating action is lost and the adjacent chains lock, the solution reverts to a gel. This "sol-gel" transformation is reversible and may be repeated.

The temperature at which thermal gelation occurs is a function of the ether substitution on the molecule. Generally speaking, the higher the methyl (and/or hydroxypropyl) substitution the lower the thermal gelation temperature. Methocel MC methylcellulose thermally gels at about 50–55C whereas Methocel 90 HG hydroxypropyl methylcellulose gels from 80 to 90C.

Biologic Properties

The Methocel cellulose ethers are highly resistant to depolymerization or degradation by enzyme systems. It has been established that the number of ether substituents per anhydroglucose unit is directly related to the degree of polymer resistance to enzymatic attack in that these substituents disrupt or disorder the enzyme-substrate relationship. Comparative studies of various systems contaminated with enzymes catalyzing the digestion of cellulose demonstrate superior stability of the Methocel polymers in terms of their viscosity uniformity and functionality.

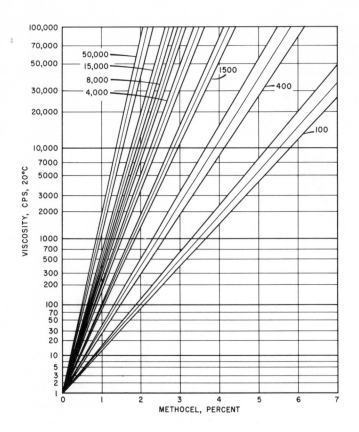

FIGURE 3.2 Viscosity-concentration chart for high-viscosity Methocel solutions.

Compatibility Properties

The methyl and hydroxypropyl methylcellulose ethers are nonionic and are not cross-linked or precipitated from solution as insoluble salts in the presence of multivalent metallic ions. In common with other hydrophilic materials, however, methylcellulose products may be gelled or salted out of solution when electrolyte concentration or level of other dissolved materials exceeds certain limits; the salt tolerance of methylcellulose is increased by modifying with hydroxypropyl substitution, thus, the Methocel HG cellulose ethers display greater salt tolerance than do Methocel MC cellulose ethers.

Organic Solubility

Although the methylcellulose ethers are generally referred to as water soluble, they do display organic solubility. The degree of organic solubility is directly related to the substitution per anhydroglucose unit and mutual water-organo soluble polymers are possible by introducing the hydroxypropoxyl and/or hydroxybutoxyl moieties. Table 3.3 summarizes some of the comparative organic solubilities.

TABLE 3.3.   Effect of Hydroxypropyl Substitution on the Solubility of Methyl Cellulose.

Chemical Name	Trademark	Per Cent Methoxyl	Per Cent Hydroxy-propoxyl	Aqueous Solubility	Solubility in 70:30 Benzene: Methanol
Methylcellulose	Methocel AS-8	4.6	—	8% caustic	Insoluble
Methylcellulose	Methocel AS-4	—	—	4% caustic	Insoluble
Methylcellulose	Methocel AS-2	14–18	—	2% caustic	Insoluble
Methylcellulose	Methocel MC	27.5–32	—	water	Insoluble
Hydroxypropyl methylcellulose	Methocel 65HG	27–29	4–7.5	water or 50% methanol, 50% water	Insoluble
Hydroxypropyl methylcellulose	Methocel 60HG	28–30	7–12	water or 80% methanol, 20% water	Soluble

The Methocel cellulose ethers are also soluble in methyl salicylate, ethyl lactate, dimethyl sulfoxide, propylene glycol (130C), and a number of other selected solvents.

Film Properties

On drying, aqueous and organic solutions of Methocel produce clear, colorless, odorless and tasteless films of high strength. These films are unaffected by animal, mineral or vegetable oils and are resistant to most organic solvents, such as: turpentine, petroleum ether, castor oil, peanut oil, mineral oil, animal fats, toluene, benzene, etc. Table 3.4 summarizes the film properties of methylcellulose films.

The hydroxypropyl methylcellulose polymers possess increased organo-solubility and thermoplasticity over the methylcellulose counterparts.

TABLE 3.4. Properties of Methylcellulose Sheeting.

	Methocel MC (unmodified)	Methocel 60HG Plasticized with Hyprin * GP25—30%
Specific gravity	1.29	1.2330
Area factor, sq in./lb/mil	21,400	22,400
Melting point, C	290–305	240–260
Moisture vapor transmission rate at 100F and 90 to 100% R.H., gm/100 sq in./ 24 hr/mil	67.5	65
Oxygen transmission rate at 75F, cc/100 sq in./24 hr/mil	25	70
Tensile strength at 75F and 50% R.H.,		
kg/sq cm	600–800	700
lb/sq in.	8500–11,400	10,000
Elongation at 75F and 50% R.H., %	10–15	45–50
Stability to ultraviolet	excellent	excellent
Resistance to oils and most solvents	excellent	excellent
Mullen Burst, psi/mil	23.9	17.9
MIT double fold 2-mil film, load	12,000	11,000
no load	32,000	25,000
Ultraviolet transmission, 2-mil film,		
400 mu, %	54.6	65.7
290 mu, %	49.0	55.3
210 mu, %	25.7	24.3

* Registered trademark of The Dow Chemical Company for its oxyalkylated glycerine.

Thermoplasticity depends upon the nature and degree of substitution and chain length of the cellulose as measured by intrinsic viscosity.

Hydroxypropyl methylcellulose with a hydroxypropyl substitution of 7 to 12 per cent has the unique property of water solubility combined with solubility in hot and cold organic solvents. When properly formulated, this product is thermoplastic and can be fabricated by a number of techniques including extrusion, injection and compression molding, hot casting and hot dipping.

Films that are heat-sealable, water-soluble and resistant to oil and greases of animal, vegetable or mineral origin can be cast from organic solvent systems. A 30–70 methanol-benzene or a 4 : 1 methanol-water mixture are examples of such systems.

The flexibility of these films depends upon plasticization, either internal or external, and upon viscosity. A variety of plasticizers are suitable, including sorbitol, glycerol, ethylene glycol, propylene glycol, triethanolamine, diethylene glycol, polypropylene glycol, and hydroxypropyl sucrose.

Alkylcellulose and hydroxyalkylcellulose films may be insolubilized by condensation reactions involving the free hydroxy groups of the anhydro-D-glucopyranose ring. Apparently only a low degree of cross-linkage is required for insolubilization to take place. A number of substituents can cause cross-linking including urea-formaldehyde resins, melamine-formaldehyde resins, polybasic acids, and dialdehydes. Table 3.5 lists some of the brand materials and their insolubilization effect on methylcellulose.

TABLE 3.5.   Insolubilization of Methylcellulose Films.

Insolubilizing Agent	Per Cent in Film	Catalyst	Amount of Catalyst	Curing Temperature °C	Curing Time Minutes	Per Cent Insoluble
Uformite 700[1]	15	Citric Acid	pH 4.5	120	20	89
Uformite 700[1]	15	HCl	pH 4.5	120	20	88
Kymene 234[2]	20	HCl	pH 2.0	120	20	96
Rhonite R-2[3]	15	NH$_4$Cl	0.75%	120	20	95

[1] Rohm & Haas Company (Resinous Products Div.).
[2] Hercules Inc.
[3] Rohm & Haas Company.

SAFETY IN FOOD USE

The premium grades of Methocel methylcellulose and Methocel hydroxypropyl methylcellulose meet the specifications of the Food Chemicals Codex. The list of food additives generally recognized as safe, and therefore exempt from the requirements of the Food Additives Amendment of 1958 (subpart B, section 121.101 of the Food Additive Regulations) includes methylcellulose USP having a methoxyl content of not less than 27.5 per cent and not more than 31.5 per cent on a dry weight basis. This listing of methylcellulose covers the whole range of products, Methocel MC premium methylcellulose.

A Food Additive Regulation (subpart D, section 121.1021) permits the use of hydroxypropyl methylcellulose N.F., (propylene glycol ether of methylcellulose N.F.) in food as an emulsifier, film former, protective colloid, stabilizer, suspending agent, or thickener in accordance with good manufacturing practice, except confectionery and except in standardized foods which do not provide for such use. This regulation covers those products described as Methocel HG premium hydroxypropyl methylcellulose.

Due to the high resistance to microorganism attack, both methylcellulose and hydroxypropyl methylcellulose can be, for all practical purposes, completely recovered from the intestinal tract after ingestion; this in itself is proof of its safety of use and lends support to their stability in a wide range of biochemical and enzyme systems.

APPLICATIONS

The applications of the methylcellulose or hydroxypropyl (and) hydroxybutyl methylcellulose ethers are keyed to their multifunctional properties. It is usually a combination of these properties which serves to demonstrate their utility. A summary of such properties is:

Water solubility	Binding
Organo solubility	pH stability
Thickening	Nonionic
Efficiencies	Lubricity
Surfactancy	Biological stability
Foam stability	Noncaloric
Emulsifier	Odorless
Protective colloids	Tasteless
Suspending agent	Colorless
Moisture retention	FDA approved
Film formation	

A combination of functional properties exhibited by Methocel cellulose ethers has led to applications in such industries as pharmaceuticals, cosmetics, foods, paints and coatings, ceramics, building and construction products, lakes and pigments, textiles, paper, packaging, plastics, adhesives, etc. This chapter will discuss only a few of these applications.

Ceramics

The refractory materials used in specialty mortars are often lacking in cohesiveness and green strength. The methylcellulose polymers impart the desired troweling properties without loss of melting point.

The uniform suspending action of methylcellulose and hydroxypropyl methylcellulose and their successes as binders in ceramic glazes are well recognized by producers of dinnerware, sanitary ware, and tile. These ethers are now utilized by many of the large manufacturers of such items.

Both methylcellulose and hydroxypropyl methylcellulose act as binders, in addition to being suspending agents. This means that the unfired glaze particles are held together tightly and are bound to the bisque surface. As a result, the skin of the glaze is toughened and fingerprinting and rub-off are reduced. As little as 0.25 per cent of these ethers based on the weight of the dry glaze has been found sufficient to impart noticeable hardening to the unfired glaze coat.

The low-viscosity types are normally recommended for most ceramic applications due to their high suspending and low thickening properties. When running and sagging present a problem, the higher viscosity types can be used. Either ether can be conveniently added as a dry powder to the ballmill when it is charged. Wet milling for several hours is sufficient to attain a complete water solution of the particles.

Paper Industry

The high strength, flexibility, clarity, and oil and wax resistance of the alkylcellulose films have proven particularly useful to the paper industry in a broad range of sizing and coating applications. These products increase the printability, uniformity and smoothness and density of all grades of paper and paperboard. Surface sizing with methylcellulose or hydroxypropyl methylcellulose results in a non-tacky surface, hence greatly minimizes sticking on the calendar rolls.

Light surface coatings of these products are especially effective in resisting the penetration of gloss ink, varnish, lacquers and waxes. Paperboard treated at the calendar stack has a surface which is characterized by high gloss, low mottling and a low ink consumption when printed with a high gloss ink.

Continuous films and coatings of alkylcellulose derivatives are impervious to practically all types of greases, oils, and solvents. Deposition of a total of two pounds of solids per thousand square feet of surface has been found to give effective greaseproofing to cellulose substrates.

In addition to its use as a size in itself, the methylcellulose and hydroxypropyl methylcellulose polymers have been added to latex coatings as a viscosity control, binding moisture retention, and film forming agent. Good scrub resistance offered by the latex film deposited from solutions containing Methocel coupled with the thickener stability over a wide pH range and in the presence of many ionic materials offers, in addition to enhanced storage stability of the latex formulation, a combination of properties important to the paper coater.

Adhesives

Leather tanning remains a fine balance of art and the efficient use of modern technology. The efficient and expensive tacking or toggling of the hides during the drawing operation has been replaced by the faster and more economical pasting of the hide to a platen. The increased number of leather pasting units in operation today has made an apparent need for an improved leather pasting adhesive.

Leather adhesives containing methylcellulose form excellent wet adhesive bonds between leather and the pasting plate. The methylcellulose paste, in contrast with other types, becomes stronger and attains maximum bonding strength at the oven temperature due to the gelation which occurs upon heating. In addition, this hot gel is elastic enough to equalize stresses in the leather and minimize looseness of structure.

Non-staining wallpaper adhesives are still dependent upon the use of cellulose ethers as their main adhesive binder. Ease of dispersibility and rapid solubility of the Methocel polymers such as Methocel 65 HG and Methocel HB coupled to their high-binding and non-staining adhesive characteristics have long defined their utility in the wallpaper paste industry. With the advent of heavy-duty wallpaper and vinyl laminate sheeting, the increased adhesive nature of the cellulose ethers have continued to play an important role in this adhesive industry.

Addition of methylcellulose or hydroxypropyl methylcellulose to adhesive bases such as those employed in the paperboard and plywood industries, offer a means of viscosity control, and moisture retention for the adhesive. The addition of the cellulose ethers to such formulations affords economic advantages with regard to the adhesive bond per pound of adhesive deposited and significantly reduces glueline starvation due to migration of the adhesive into the porous substrates.

Paints

The nonionic hydroxypropyl methylcellulose polymers are important ingredients in water based paints of either the dry or emulsion type. Hydroxypropyl methylcellulose provides good viscosity stability over long storage periods, reduces problems of pH control in the finished paint and promotes excellent pigment dispersion and stability through its suspension properties. In general, 1 to 2 per cent based on the weight of paint solids will provide satisfactory results.

Methylcellulose is a critical ingredient in multi-color finish formulations through its use as a protective colloid and stabilizing agent, forming a protective film around individual particles of coating materials and causing them to repel each other and remain distinct. It is now possible to include within a single formulation three or more different colors which although intermixed, remain separate and dry to yield a multi-colored coating upon application by conventional methods.

Paint Removers

If a paint stripper is to be effective, it must adhere to vertical surfaces with a minimum of running and sagging. Present demands for specialized paint strippers with an ever-increasing number of additives require a thickener to be compatible with a broad range of materials.

Hydroxypropyl methylcellulose and hydroxybutyl methylcellulose are very effective thickeners for methylene chloride paint strippers because of their good organic solubility. They also offer the advantage of good compatibility and low sensitivity to water content.

Hydroxypropyl methylcellulose can be used in both flush-off and scrape-off formulations. The flush-off type raises the paint film which may then be removed by flushing with a stream of water. This formulation is primarily for industrial plant removal from metal or from wood where slight staining is not important. The second type of remover loosens paint films for removal by scraping. It has been widely marketed in small packages for home use.

The use of Methocel 90 HG hydroxypropyl methylcellulose as an emulsion paint stripper has offered a means of preparing water based emulsions containing methylene chloride through the combination of properties such as water solubility, organic compatibility, thickening efficiency and emulsification efficiency of the cellulose ether.

Pharmaceutical Products

The pharmaceutical industry has found methylcellulose and hydroxypropyl methylcellulose products to be valuable aids in a variety of applications. They have, for example, found extensive applications as bulk laxatives because of their unique gelling and solubility characteristics which result in more effective bulking action in the large intestine. Also, under equilibrium conditions at body temperature, Methocel yields a soft gel in the intestines. Methocel is nonionic so there is no danger of introducing additional minerals into the body or removing essential minerals from it.

Many medical applications take advantage of the excellent suspending and wetting properties of methylcellulose products. The use of methylcellulose to suspend barium sulfate in X-ray radiography techniques to obtain a more uniform distribution of the barium sulfate and a sharper definition in X-ray photographs is an interesting example. High viscosity methylcellulose has proved extremely valuable as a suspending agent in neocalamine and bismuth type preparations.

The emulsion stabilizing properties of the nonionic methylcellulose and hydroxypropyl methylcellulose ethers are useful in many ointments, creams, emulsions, and suspensions. In all these applications, the cellulose polymers serve as curing agents for the medicants and also hold them on the surface of the skin.

The combination of organic solubility while retaining water solubility coupled to the unique property of high strength film formation, has placed Methocel cellulose ethers as a leader in the field of film coatings of pharmaceutical tablets. Deposition of water soluble films from organic solvents onto tablets containing water susceptible drugs offer a unique and economical coating for pharmaceutical tablets and granules.

Cosmetics

The nonionic methylcellulose and hydroxypropyl methylcellulose ethers improve the smoothness of finished cosmetics because of their unique stabilizing and thickening action. When properly plasticized, these materials function as film forming materials and pigment binders useful in the manufacture of makeup preparations.

Other cosmetic preparations formulated with these polymers include hand creams, vanishing creams, shampoos, hairdressings, depilatories, shaving creams, hand lotions, bubble bath liquids, and sun creams. Since the Methocel cellulose ethers provide a barrier against oil materials, they have been used in protective creams to guard against irritants ranging from tear gas to paint.

N. C. Eastman
J. K. Rose

Technical Center
Union Carbide Corporation
South Charleston, West Virginia

Hydroxyethylcellulose

Who would want water soluble ship log books! And why? The Navy did at one time; so that log books could not be recovered from sunken ships by a wartime enemy. The then little known hydroxyethylcellulose (HEC) was selected and developed for this use. Being fibrous, it could be made into sheets; and being both water soluble and tolerant of salt, the pages would disintegrate in salt water. By now, these properties of water solubility and tolerance of other solutes coupled with solution viscosity building have resulted in many commercial uses for this modified natural polymer.

Hydroxyethylcellulose is a nonionic water-soluble polymer made by chemically reacting cellulose with ethylene oxide. This resin has the ability to thicken, suspend, bind, emulsify, form films, stabilize, disperse, retain water, or provide protective colloid action. It is readily soluble in either hot or cold water and can be used to prepare solutions with a wide range of viscosities. These solutions have outstanding tolerance for dissolved electrolytes. Solutions of the high viscosity grades of HEC are pseudoplastic, i.e., their viscosities vary depending on the rate of shear applied in the viscosity determination.

In film-forming applications, HEC may be used alone to produce a water-soluble film, or it may be reacted with other chemicals to produce a film that is insoluble in both cold and boiling water.

The thickening property of HEC is utilized in paints and cosmetics to create products with a desired body to satisfy esthetic as well as performance needs. Thickened water is more efficient than water itself in applications such as forest fire fighting and oil well water flooding. Thickening combined with pseudoplasticity in HEC gives hair shampoos which pour "rich and heavy" from the container. Yet these shampoos thin out, feel wet, and disperse easily when rubbed between the hands and applied to the hair. In latex paints, these two properties give a good heavy body, so the paint stays on the brush, flows out easily on brushing, and then levels out to eliminate brush marks.

Because HEC is nonionic, it is stable in solutions with high concentrations of salts. It can be used in electroplating, for example, where it imparts improved brightness and uniformity to the plating, and yet is not precipitated by the high concentration of salts in the electroplating bath. In cosmetics, HEC can be used to thicken underarm deodorants despite the high salts levels of such products.

Strong continuous films of HEC can be formed from water solutions on many substrates. In paper manufacturing, such coatings are impervious to oils, greases, and most solvents. This property also contributes to excellent ink holdout when applied in paper sizing formulations. In textiles, HEC can serve as a warp size to protect fibers from mechanical abuse. The film-forming property can be used advantageously as a temporary protective coating for various products during processing and shipping. When protection is no longer needed, the coating can be washed off.

When it is desired to maintain the water content of formulations at a desired level, HEC can help. For example, unless water-retaining and binding properties are built in, cement-based mortars lose adhesion and strength, and ceramic powders lose plasticity under pressure.

MANUFACTURE OF HEC

Cellulose is a water-insoluble polymer composed of repeating anhydroglucose units. To manufacture HEC, a highly purified form of cellulose is reacted with sodium hydroxide to produce a swollen alkali cellulose, which, in turn, is reacted with ethylene oxide. In hydroxyethylcellulose ethers, the hydrogen atoms in the hydroxyl groups of cellulose are replaced by the hydroxyethyl groups which confer water solubility on the product. After hydroxyethylation, the product is purified and ground to a fine powder and sold in this country by Union Carbide Corporation and by Hercules Inc. under the trademarks Cellosize and Natrosol, respectively. Figure 4.1 shows

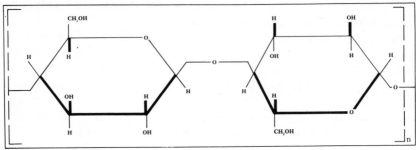

FIGURE 4.1   Structure of cellulose.

the structure of cellulose and Figure 4.2 indicates one of the possible arrangements of the substituent hydroxyethyl groups.

The placement of the hydroxyethyl substituents on the cellulose chain is described by the terms "degree of substitution" (DS) and "molar substitution" (MS). The degree of substitution designates the average number

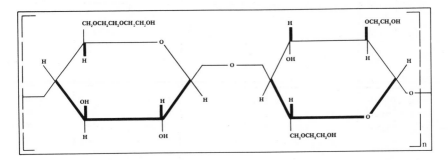

FIGURE 4.2 Structure of hydroxyethylcellulose — one of the possible arrangements.

of substituted hydroxyl positions on each anhydroglucose unit of the cellulose molecule. Since each anhydroglucose unit has three hydroxyl groups (Figure 4.1), the maximum value for DS is 3.

Molar substitution is defined as the average number of ethylene oxide molecules which have been substituted onto each anhydroglucose unit. Once a hydroxyethyl group is attached, it can itself react further with additional ethylene oxide in an end to end formation. This reaction can continue as long as ethylene oxide is available; there is no theoretical limit for MS. A minimum MS value near 1.3 is required for good water solubility.

The solution viscosity of HEC can be varied over a wide range by changing the molecular weight of the cellulose backbone. It is, therefore, possible to manufacture a large number of different viscosity grades. Table 4.1 shows standard grades and types commercially available from one company and their respective viscosity ranges in aqueous solution; specification limits are defined by the Hoeppler viscosimeter data, with approximate Brookfield ranges included for comparison.

Table 4.2 shows some typical physical properties of the undissolved powdered HEC regardless of solution viscosity type.

APPLICATIONS OF HEC

Resins based on HEC are approved by the United States Food and Drug Administration for use in indirect food applications such as food packaging

TABLE 4.1 Viscosity ranges for various grades of cellosize hydroxyethylcellulose in aqueous solution.

HEC Type	Viscosity Grade	Concentration Weight % on Dry Basis*	Specification Limits Hoeppler Viscosity, cps at 20°C.		Corresponding LVT Brookfield Viscosity cps at 25°C. (Approximate)		Spindle	
			L Range	H Range	L Range	H Range	Number	RPM
WP	02	5	7–13	14–20	7–14	14–20	1	60
WP	09	5	80–119	120–160	60–100	100–140	1	30
and	3	5	250–324	325–400	220–285	285–350	2	60
QP	40	2	80–112	113–145	70–110	110–150	1	30
	300	2	250–324	325–400	250–325	325–400	2	60
	4400	2	4750–6174	6175–7600	4200–4700	4700–5200	4	60
QP	15,000	2	16,000–19,999	20,000–24,000	15,000–18,000	18,000–21,000	4	12
	30,000	1	480–639	640–800	950–1230	1230–1500	3	60
	52,000	1	1250–1599	1600–1950	1500–1800	1800–2100	3	60
	100M	1	(one range only)	2250–3000	2500–3000		4	60
					3000–4000		3	30

*CELLOSIZE HEC contains from about 3% to not more than 5% volatiles when packaged. The weight of CELLOSIZE HEC used to prepare these solutions was adjusted to compensate for the volatiles.

TABLE 4.2 Typical properties of powdered HEC.

Ash Content, calculated	
as % by wt. Na_2CO_3	2.5
as % by wt. Na_2SO_4	3.5
Apparent Density, lb./ft.³	22 to 38
Color	Cream to white
Decomposition Temperature	Approximately 400°F.
Particle size	Powdered
Softening Point	>285°F.
Specific Gravity, (20/20°C.)	1.38-1.40
Volatile Matter	<5% by wt.

adhesives and coatings, but HEC itself has not been cleared for use as a direct food additive.

The nonionic nature of HEC, and its ability to thicken, suspend, bind, emulsify, form films, stabilize, disperse, retain water, or act as a protective colloid has made it the key to many industrial applications.

Agriculture

HEC can be used as an adjuvant in a variety of agricultural formulations. Low concentrations of HEC effectively suspend solid toxicants in water-based sprays. When used in a spray, HEC helps bind the toxicant to the foliage. As a film-former, it can be useful as a seed coating. As a thickener for spray emulsions, it reduces drift. Thus, sprays can be placed directly on foliage with greatly increased efficiency.

Cosmetics

HEC is an effective film-former, binder, thickener, stabilizer, and dispersant in shampoos, hair sprays, neutralizers, creams, and lotions. Its solubility at elevated temperatures simplifies and speeds up production techniques. The body, smoothness, and silkiness of preparations based on HEC are attractive consumer selling features.

Latex Manufacture

The lower viscosity grades of HEC are recommended as the protective colloid in the preparation of vinyl acetate homopolymer and copolymer latexes. They contribute good freeze-thaw and mechanical and electrolyte stability.

Paint Thickening

Most latex suppliers recommend the use of HEC in their suggested paint formulations because of its ease of dissolving, low-foaming characteristics, thickening efficiency, and contribution to color development and stabilization. Since HEC is widely employed as a protective colloid in emulsion polymerization, its use in subsequent paint thickening results in a more uniformly integrated film.

Paper

The printing industry has found HEC to be a useful gloss and ink hold-out size for paper and paperboard. It gives excellent hold-out for oil-based inks, varnishes, and lacquers. Advantages of printing paper sized with HEC include superior definition of printed images, lower cost because of penetration of the top coat, and high gloss. It can be applied to paper or paperboard at either the size press or the calendar stack. In paper sizing, 0.1 to 0.5 pounds per 1,000 square feet is the usual application.

The use of HEC also contributes to improved grease resistance. For oil- and grease-proof coatings, about 2 pounds per 1,000 square feet of surface are recommended. Coatings may be applied by blade, air-knife, or roll coating. The very low viscosity HEC (*ca.* 10 cps at 5 per cent concentration) is especially useful since it can be applied from a concentrated solution at a workable viscosity. A single application is sufficient to give a continuous coat.

Some of the other desirable properties of HEC in paper applications are its ready solubility in water; compatibility with most gums, resins, and inorganic salts; low biochemical oxygen demand; low foaming tendency; its ability to form clear films; and its non-interference with the recovery of broke.

Textiles

Solutions of HEC make useful warp sizes which can be removed from the fiber by water-washing. Because of the low biochemical oxygen demand of HEC, wash-water disposal problems are reduced. As a carrier for pigments and colors, HEC contributes to good penetration and sharpness of pattern. In combination with other resins, HEC has found application in textile finishes. It is also used to thicken latexes in textile formulations.

Electroplating and Electro-Refining

The efficient protective colloid action of HEC is unaffected by the high concentration of electrolytes used in plating baths. The result is brighter plating, especially cadmium plating, even over irregular surfaces. It is equally effective in hot or cold baths. In the electrorefining of copper and other metals, HEC helps attain smooth uniform deposition of the metal.

Other Applications

HEC is also useful in the following:

Adhesives. Thickener in latex adhesive formulations.

Cement. Retarder and moisture retaining agent.

Ceramics. Green strength binder and water-retaining agent in a dry molding and ceramic glazes.

Detergents. Thickener and protective colloid in liquid detergents and waterless hand cleaners.

Electrical. Sizing agent for asbestos in the manufacture of cables. Nonionic component of plastic covers.

Fire Fighting. Additive to enhance the blanketing properties of fire-fighting foam. Useful in "thickened water" for fire fighting.

Foundries. Additive to improve the green strength and reduce collapsibility in cement sand and sodium silicate sand systems.

Glass Fibers. Water-soluble forming size and binder.

Inks. For the production of water-based duplicating inks that dry rapidly without offset or bleeding.

Leather. Finishing and binding agent in leather pastes.

Microscopy. Film-forming, dispersing agent to prepare microscopic slides; thickener, to reduce Brownian movement in aqueous substrates.

Mining. Component in spray mixtures to avoid losses from mining concentrates during storage.

Oil Wells. Additive in oil well cements.

Photography. Thickening agent in film processing fluids with high salt concentrations.

Rubber. Thickener in rubber latex and as a mold release agent.

Tobacco. Binding agent for reconstituted tobacco leaf.

Wallboard. Component of emulsions for surface treatment to improve release from press and to enhance painting properties.

Wallpaper Paste. Wallpaper paste ingredient.

PROPERTIES OF POWDERED HEC

Toxicological

Toxicological studies with hydroxyethylcellulose indicate that it is a product with apparently low oral toxicity. Inclusion in the rat diet at a level of 5 per cent for 90 days caused no detectable harm. HEC is believed to be nonirritating to the human skin and of low sensitizing potential. Contact with the human eye may be expected to cause a reaction no more severe than a moderate degree of inflammation.

Indirect evidence supports the belief that HEC is neither absorbed nor hydrolyzed in the gastrointestinal tract. A parental and an F_1 generation of Wistar strain albino rats were maintained for two years upon diets containing HEC. Fifty-two rats for each dosage level and control were fed diets containing HEC in concentrations of 5, 1 and 0.2 per cent. The resulting mean dosages were 2.31, 0.41, and 0.09 gram per kilogram per day respectively. The dosages had no adverse effects, except that the food intake of rats eating the 5 per cent diet was one-tenth greater than the animals in the three other groups.

Explosibility

Dusts of HEC are explosive if mixed with air in the critical proportions and in the presence of an ignition source. These dusts represent a hazard quite similar to that of other cellulosic derivatives, and to many widely used organic solids. Normal good housekeeping procedures for control of dusts should be observed.

Hygroscopicity

Storage in open or loosely capped containers will change the moisture content of HEC to an equilibrium value determined by the relative humidity of the environment. There may be a loss of moisture in dry weather, and a gain in humid weather. The effect of relative humidity on the equilibrium moisture content of HEC is shown in Figure 4.3.

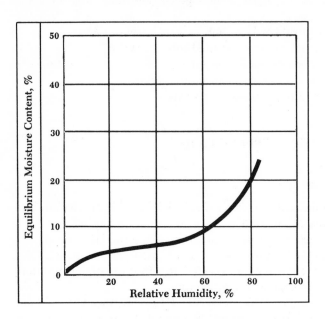

FIGURE 4.3   Effect of relative humidity on the equilibrium moisture content of hydroxyethylcellulose at 25C.

Solubility in Organic Solvents

Water soluble HEC is insoluble in most organic solvents as shown in Table 4.3. In a few of the polar solvents, those generally miscible with water, it is either swollen or partially soluble.

AQUEOUS SOLUTIONS

Clear, viscous, bubble-free solutions can be prepared with ease on either plant or laboratory scale once the operator has acquired a slight amount of experience. This has not always been true. Most commercial HEC, like instant coffee, instant puddings, and powdered milk, has been very slightly modified in order to make it easily dissolvable; its true or real solubility is

TABLE 4.3 Solubility of hydroxyethylcellulose in organic solvents.

SOLVENT	SOLUBILITY
A. Hydrocarbons	
Xylene	I
Benzene	I
Petrolene	I
Kerosene	I
B. Chlorinated Hydrocarbons	
Chlorobenzene	I
Carbon Tetrachloride	I
Trichloroethylene	I
Ethylene Dichloride	I
C. Alcohols	
Butanol	I
Ethanol (95%)	I
Methyl CELLOSOLVE	I
Methanol	P
D. Aldehydes	
Butyraldehyde	P
Formalin	S
E. Ketones	
Acetone	I
Diethyl Ketone	I
F. Acids	
Acetic Acid	P
Formic Acid	S
G. Esters	
n-Amyl Acetate	I
Ethyl Acetate	I
H. Amines	
Ethylene Diamine	S
Pyridine	I
Diethylene Triamine	S
I. Ethers	
Isopropyl Ether	I
Ethyl Ether	I
1, 4-Dioxane	I
CARBITOL Solvent	I
J. Oils	
Mineral Oil	I
Cotton Seed Oil	I
Lard Oil	I
Linseed Oil	I
K. Other	
Dimethyl Formamide	S
Dimethyl Acetamide	S
Dimethyl Sulfoxide	S

S=Soluble   I=Insoluble   P=Partially soluble

not affected, only its ease of dissolving is changed. The name "hydroxy-ethylcellulose" and the abbreviation "HEC" are used in this chapter to designate either or both the modified and unmodified resin unless specifically designated otherwise. Once in solution, there appears to be no difference between the two types.

Solutions of the easily dissolvable HEC may be prepared by dumping the resin into mildly agitated water at ambient temperature. The resin is wetted and dispersed easily forming a thin or non-viscous, cloudy slurry. No visible change occurs immediately, but after a short period (sometimes called "hydration time") the slurry begins to thicken and to become less cloudy. The mix may pass through a viscosity peak before it levels out at a stable viscosity; at about the same time the solution becomes clear and the dis-solving is completed.

The initial value of the easily dissolvable character is that it allows the resin to be quickly and easily dispersed into a lump-free dispersion with only moderate agitation. Thereafter only sufficient agitation to maintain the resin in suspension is required except for the highest viscosity types which do require some further agitation to become smooth solutions.

The second value is that the user is given on-site control of both the hydration and dissolving times by means of either temperature or solution pH adjustments. The times may be shortened by warming and lengthened by cooling. The times are also shortened by increasing the pH of the solu-tion; in fact the easily dissolving HEC acts like the unimproved resin at a high pH level. Conversely, mild acidification lengthens the times, while high acidity, e.g. one per cent sulfuric acid, decreases the times. Thus the resin can be dispersed readily in neutral water, and then dissolved quickly by adding either a basic or an acid component of the formulation.

A third value is that, by judicious use of these special dissolving proper-ties, a user can introduce dry HEC into a formulation or process without the necessity of having previously prepared a separate stock solution of the resin. The resin can be uniformly dispersed into many formulations without immediately increasing their viscosities, then, later and when planned, viscosity build takes place. Savings in process time and equipment are apparent.

Either vigorous agitation or a long time, or both, are normally required for dissolving the unmodified type of HEC. Since dissolving and viscosity build start immediately, this type of resin is prone to extensive lump forma-tion during dissolving. Sifting the resin onto vigorously agitated water helps to reduce lump formation and thereby to speed the dissolving process. The lumping and dissolving problem can sometimes be alleviated by dis-persing the resin in another solid or a water soluble liquid. Vigorous agita-tion is still required. Another technique involves the addition of a surfactant to the water. This technique also requires vigorous agitation.

TABLE 4.4 Typical properties of aqueous solutions of hydroxyethylcellulose.

Refractive Index, 2% solution, 20°C.	1.336
Specific Gravity 2% solution, g/ml, 20°C.	1.0033
Surface Tension, at 25°C. 0.01 to 1.0% solution, dynes/cm.	63-69
Color, 2% solution	30 Pt-Co
pH, 2% solution	6-7
Freezing Point, 2% solution	0°C.
Biological Oxygen Demand, 2% solution	4600 p.p.m.

PROPERTIES OF SOLUTIONS

Perhaps the most striking observation on polymer solutions is the tremendous increase in viscosity imparted to a non-viscous solvent by a small amount of a dissolved polymer. It is almost equally striking that the viscosity of any given polymer solution is dependent upon the force being applied to the solution as it is being used or as its viscosity is measured. HEC is no exception.

Effect of Variables on Viscosity

Almost any solution viscosity can be achieved using HEC. In addition to the large range of commercially available viscosity types (see Table 4.1), the solution viscosity of a single lot is dependent on the shear rate employed in the measurement, on the solution concentration, on the solution temperature, and on the solution pH.

Viscosity types HEC is manufactured in a wide range of solution viscosity types or grades. Solution viscosity is governed by the chain length of the cellulose backbone. This is essentially the only difference between viscosity types.

Shear rate The solutions of the medium and high viscosity grades of HEC are non-Newtonian and show a high degree of pseudoplasticity, i.e. the measured viscosity depends upon the shear rate at which it is measured. For example, a 2 per cent solution of a medium viscosity grade HEC may yield a 20C Hoeppler viscosity of 5,000 centipoises. The same solution may yield 25C Brookfield viscosities of 12,000, 7,500, or 4,600 cps, depending on whether the viscometer was operated at 0.3, 12, or

60 rpm. The solutions of the low viscosity types show a low degree of pseudoplasticity and are more nearly Newtonian. This trend appears in Figures 4.4 and 4.5, and is shown more clearly by the linear viscosity scale used in Figure 4.6.

The molecular arrangement of hydroxyethylcellulose chains in solution is

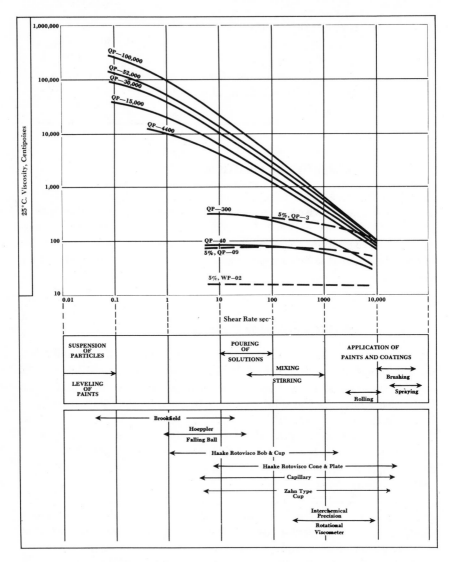

FIGURE 4.4 Typical solution viscosity-shear rate relationship (log scale) for 2 per cent solution concentration (except where indicated) of hydroxyethylcellulose.

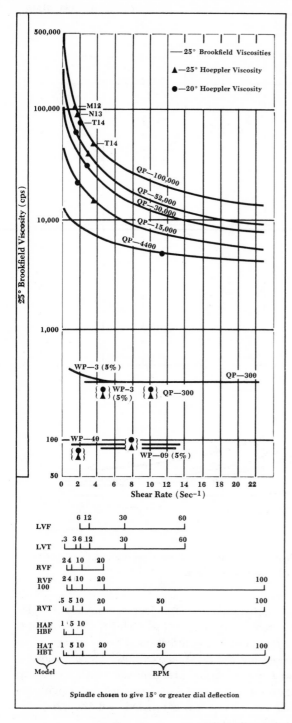

FIGURE 4.5 Brookfield-Hoeppler viscosity correlation for 2 per cent (except where indicated) concentration of hydroxyethylcellulose.

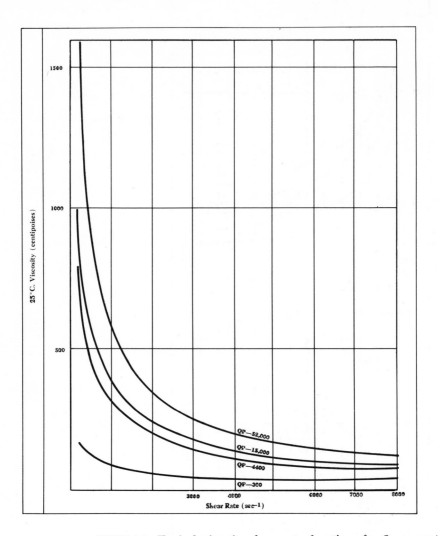

FIGURE 4.6 Typical viscosity-shear rate functions for 2 per cent solutions of hydroxyethylcellulose.

random at low rates of shear, this results in a high degree of chain entanglement and consequent high viscosity. At high rates of shear, the molecules tend to become oriented with respect to the direction of flow (analogous to logs in a river), thereby decreasing the resistance to flow. Thus, viscosity, defined as the ratio of shear stress to shear rate, decreases with increasing shear rate as shown in Figures 4.4, 4.5 and 4.6. As molecular weight decreases, the shorter polymer chains are less entangled and their pseudoplastic character becomes less pronounced.

Shear stability Excellent shear stability is exhibited by all grades of HEC. Viscosity measurements have been obtained in laboratory equipment immediately before and after 15-minute exposures to a high shear rate of 8,200 reciprocal seconds. No change in the viscosities of these 2 per cent solutions was observed. When solutions of HEC are subjected to the high shear rates inherent in some industrial equipment, viscosity stability is still unaffected.

Concentration A tremendous increase in solution viscosity results from even a moderate increase in solution concentration. In fact, the increase is so great, that viscosity versus concentration graphs conventionally have the viscosity plotted on a log scale and concentration on a linear scale (see Figure 4.7). Since the increase is so large, a single target viscosity can be achieved with a number of different viscosity grade resins merely by choosing the appropriate solution concentration. However, while the single shear rate viscosities of these solutions is the same, their flow properties can differ, one solution being more pseudoplastic or non-Newtonian than another.

Temperature Increasing the temperature of a solution of HEC reversably reduces the solution viscosity since cooling the solution to the original temperature restores original viscosity. This effect, illustrated in Figure 4.8, is the only influence temperature has on solutions of HEC. The solutions may be subjected to freeze-thaw conditions, may be used at high temperature, may even be boiled without precipitation, gelling, or other problems.

pH Variations in pH between about 2 and 12 have little effect on the viscosity of solutions of HEC. Solution viscosities tend to be lower beyond these limits. They may also be less stable if hydrolysis occurs at low pH, or if oxidation occurs at high pH. Such reactions are characteristic of many polymers.

Blending for Solution Viscosity

Commercially manufactured HEC is available in specific viscosity ranges (see Table 4.1); however, the user may obtain any intermediate viscosity by blending resin of two different viscosity grades. He may either dry blend two resins or dissolve the resins simultaneously. Blend viscosity and composition relationships may be approximated by either an equation or by a graphical procedure employing a blending curve, or less preferably, a straight edge. Use of either the equation or the straight edge on the graph gives weighted geometric average viscosities.

$$\log V_{AB} = f_A \times \log V_A + f_B \times \log V_B$$

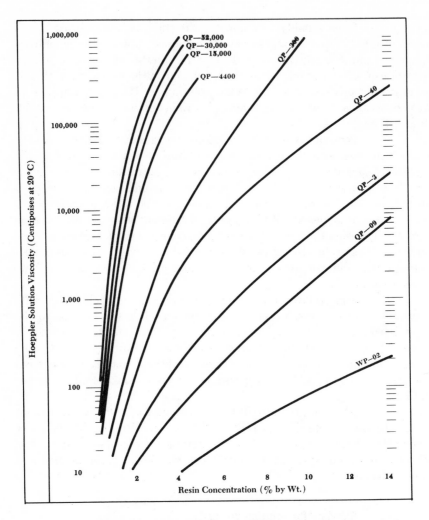

FIGURE 4.7 Typical effect of HEC concentration on solution viscosity.

where A and B = subscripts denoting resin A, resin B, or a mixture of the two.

V = solution viscosity

f = weight fraction, i.e., weight of indicated resin divided by total weight of both resins.

When the viscosity of one resin does not exceed 1.5 times the viscosity of the other resin, the equation or the straight edge may be used as well as the

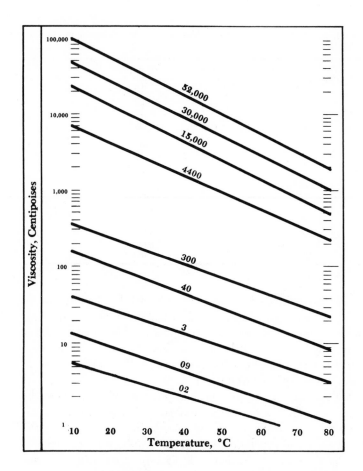

FIGURE 4.8 Effect of temperature on viscosity for Cellosize HEC WP and QP grades; average Hoeppler viscosity of 2 per cent solutions at various temperatures.

curve. The authors prefer to use the blending curve when the two resins of the proposed blend vary more widely in their respective viscosities. The viscosities of actual blends are usually slightly higher than the geometric averages; the blending curve (with its variation in curvature) reasonably approximates this difference.

A blending curve may be constructed with the data shown in Table 4.5 and a sheet of semilog paper. A smooth curve is drawn on the semilog paper laid out as shown in Figure 4.9. The curve is transferred to transparent paper or clear plastic with an "X" marked on the zero concentration-10 centipoise point in order to serve as a starting point when using the curve.

TABLE 4.5 Data to construct viscosity blending curve for solutions of hydroxyethyl - cellulose.

Blend Composition % of High Viscosity Polymer	Viscosity Scale
0	10.0
10	20.1
20	40.1
25	56.3
30	77.7
40	147
50	268
60	468
70	775
75	980
80	1220
85	1500
90	1800
95	2130
100	2500

A blend may now be estimated for any two lots of HEC having known solution viscosities (measured at the same concentration and other identical conditions). The position of the lower solution viscosity is noted on the A ordinate of the prepared graph and the higher viscosity on the B ordinate. The blending curve is then placed on the graph so that the starting point X falls on the lower viscosity on ordinate A and the curve crosses the B ordinate at the higher viscosity (see example in Figure 4.9). Note that the curve should be convex up. The curve now indicates the approximate composition and viscosity relationship of any mixture of the two resins, i.e. the viscosity of any given blend can be read from the graph and vice-versa.

The curve can be used under a rather wide variety of conditions; it has also been used without modification for carboxymethylcellulose.

BIOLOGICAL STABILITY

Bacteria or fungi may be introduced inadvertently with water or other ingredients used when preparing solutions of HEC. Materials which have been contaminated for some time may contain appreciable concentrations of the enzymes produced by these micro organisms. These enzymes, in turn, catalyze the degradation of many polymers. Solutions of HEC are more stable against micro biological degradation than natural gums; but like all cellulosic water-soluble polymers, they are susceptible. Significant viscosity losses can occur under severe conditions.

Microbiological spoilage can be arrested by sterilizing the solutions at 100C for a minute or two. If the solutions are stored under aseptic condi-

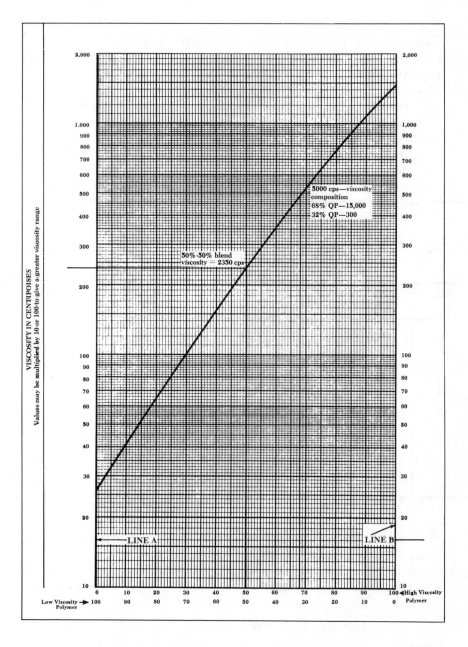

FIGURE 4.9 Blending graph for Cellosize hydroxyethylcellulose. Uses blending curve described under section on "Blending for Solution Viscosity."

tions, no further loss in viscosity occurs. The sterilization technique will not materially affect the viscosity of solutions, and can be used to prevent enzymatic attack.

However, in most commercial applications, solutions cannot be stored under aseptic conditions and this sterilization technique becomes impractical. As an alternative, a preservative or microbicide is used to inhibit the growth of microorganisms in solutions of cellulose ethers. The mercurial microbiocides have been found to be effective preservatives for solutions of HEC, and phenylmercuric acetate (PMA) is recommended where an extended shelf life is required. An adequate level of PMA should be introduced at the earliest possible moment. Table 4.6 shows an example of the use of

TABLE 4.6   Effect of preservative on solutions of hydroxyethylcellulose.

CELLOSIZE HEC QP-4400 Solution Innoculated
with 10 PPM of Enzyme-Cellase and a Preservative (1)

Time Days	No Preservative Viscosity in cps	No Preservative pH	With PMA-30[2] Viscosity in cps	With PMA-30 pH
0	4400	6.1	4400	6.1
1	100	6.0	4300	6.1
2	100	6.0	4300	6.0
3	–	–	4700	6.1
7	–	–	4400	6.1
11	–	–	4600	6.1
30	–	–	4700	6.0

(1) PMA-30—Phenyl mercuric acetate, 30% active. (2) Added at 250 ppm.

PMA-30 to inhibit the action of the cellulase "Cellase-100" (Wallerstine Company) over a 30-day period.

Care is required in selecting and using preservatives for food-related applications of HEC. Mercurials are not recommended on basis of toxicity.

AQUEOUS SOLUTION COMPATIBILITIES

HEC is at least partially compatible with most water-soluble gums and resins in common use (see Table 4.7). It can be combined with these materials to form clear, homogeneous solutions. However solution viscosities are not always predictable depending on choice of gum and concentration of

TABLE 4.7 Compatibility of aqueous solutions of hydroxyethylcellulose with gums and resins.

Compatible	
Dextrin	Gum Karaya
Borated Dextrin	Gum Tragacanth
Casein	Sodium Alginate
Gelatin	Methyl Cellulose
Gum Arabic	Polyvinyl Alcohol
Sodium Carboxymethyl Cellulose	

Partly Compatible
Starch

Incompatible
Zein

both resins. Thus the formulator has at his command many combinations from which to select the best system for his needs.

Among the water-soluble gums and resins listed in Table 4.7 the soluble metal salts of alginic acid have a synergistic effect on the solution viscosity of HEC, small amounts increasing the viscosity several fold. This combination is particularly effective in producing gels.

HEC can be salted out of solution like other organic solutes, but its salt tolerance is much greater than most other water-soluble cellulose derivatives.

Being an ether-alcohol, HEC is not ionizable in aqueous media. It cannot be precipitated from solution by the reaction with heavy metal ions as can anionic cellulosics. The nonionic character of HEC makes it an outstanding colloidal thickener for solutions containing high concentrations of electrolytes. In general, lower-viscosity grades of HEC tolerate higher concentrations of salt than do the higher viscosity grades. Data on the compatibility of HEC with higher concentrations of salts are given in Table 4.8. The polymer is compatible with 10 per cent solutions of all salts listed in the table.

Surface Activity

Hydroxyethylcellulose is extensively used to stabilize oil in water emulsions, yet it does not itself promote foaming problems. HEC is a very mild surfactant; as a typical example, the presence of only 0.01 per cent resin

TABLE 4.8 Compatibility of aqueous solutions of hydroxyethylcellulose with inorganic salts.

Saturated solutions were tested except where concentration at saturation exceeded 50 per cent.
To 15 grams of each salt solution, 1 ml. of the solution of CELLOSIZE Hydroxyethyl Cellulose was added.

Salt	Salt Concentration*	Results Observed With Solutions of	
		10% WP-09	2% WP-4400
Carbonate, Sodium	50%	Ppt[a]	Ppt
Chloride, Ammonium	Saturated	No ppt	No ppt
Chloride, Calcium	Saturated	No ppt	No ppt
Chloride, Ferric	50%	No ppt	No ppt
Chloride, Ferrous	50%	No ppt	No ppt
Chloride, Magnesium	Saturated	No ppt	No ppt
Chloride, Sodium	Saturated	No ppt	No ppt
Chloride, Stannic	Saturated	No ppt	No ppt
Chloride, Zinc	50%	No ppt	No ppt
Dichromate, Sodium	50%	No ppt	No ppt
Ferricyanide, Potassium	Saturated	No ppt	V sl ppt[b]
Ferrocyanide, Potassium	Saturated	Ppt	Ppt
Metasulfite, Potassium	Saturated	No ppt	No ppt

Salt	Concentration		
Nitrate, Aluminum	Saturated	No ppt	No ppt
Nitrate, Ammonium	Saturated	No ppt	No ppt
Nitrate, Calcium	Saturated	No ppt	No ppt
Nitrate, Chromic	Saturated	No ppt	No ppt
Nitrate, Magnesium	Saturated	No ppt	No ppt
Nitrate, Silver	50%	No ppt	Sl ppt[c]
Nitrate, Sodium	Saturated	No ppt	No ppt
Nitrate, Zinc	Saturated	No ppt	No ppt
Perborate, Sodium	Saturated	No ppt	No ppt
Phosphate, Disodium	Saturated	Ppt	Ppt
Sulfate, Aluminum	Saturated	Ppt	Ppt
Sulfate, Ammonium	Saturated	Ppt	Ppt
Sulfate, Chromic	Saturated	Ppt	Ppt
Sulfate, Ferric	Saturated	No ppt	No ppt
Sulfate, Magnesium	Saturated	Ppt	Ppt
Sulfate, Sodium	Saturated	Ppt	Ppt
Sulfate, Zinc	Saturated	Ppt	Ppt
Sulfite, Sodium	Saturated	Ppt	Ppt
Thiosulfate, Sodium	Saturated	Ppt	Ppt

a. Precipitation   b. Very Slight Precipitation   c. Slight Precipitation   °At room temperature lowered the surface tension of water from 72 to 66 dynes/cm. But increasing the concentration to one per cent has little further effect, the surface tension being lowered only to 65 dynes/cm. Thus, HEC is not an emulsification agent or foam producing agent; it does tend to stabilize emulsions and foams caused by other agents. Foaming problems are not generally introduced by use of HEC; in fact in a few applications, the HEC appears to actually hinder foaming. However, if foaming does raise problems, these can usually be overcome by use of a small amount (0.2 per cent) of one of several commercial water-dispersible defoamers.

MAKING HEC FILMS

Films with good clarity and moderate strength can be prepared from solutions of HEC. They possess good oil and grease resistance and are insoluble in nearly all organic solvents.

By appropriate modification with plasticizers, films with a wide variety of physical and chemical properties can be produced. Depending upon the solution formulation, films can be produced which are soluble in cold and hot water while others are insoluble in cold water and even in boiling water. Films can be made with good adhesion to a variety of surfaces; or they can be made to be readily strippable.

Water-soluble films are usually prepared by evaporating solutions of the appropriate polymer on a substrate. The unplasticized film possesses those general properties shown in Table 4.9.

TABLE 4.9   Properties of unplasticized hydroxyethylcellulose films.

Density, g/cc	1.38-1.40
Tensile Modulus, psi	4100–4700
Elongation to break, %	5-7
Elastic Modulus, psi	177,000–195,000
Color	Colorless

For applications that require greater flexibility and elongation, films based on HEC can be plasticized. By adding 5 to 30 weight per cent plasticizer, film elongation and flexibility are increased. Plasticizers that have proven effective include: glycerol, ethanolamines, glycols, sorbitol, sulfonated oil, and polyglycols.

Plasticizers have a profound effect on the impact resistance of HEC films. A comparison of the impact resistance of representative plasticized and un-plasticized films of HEC at different relative humidities is shown in Table 4.10.

TABLE 4.10   Impact resistance of hydroxyethylcellulose films.

	Impact Resistance ($ft\text{-}lbs/in^2$)	
Film	10% Rel. Hum. 10°C	50% Rel. Hum. 5°C
CELLOSIZE HEC QP-09	7	13
CELLOSIZE HEC QP-09+ 20% diethylene glycol	22	47

Water-insoluble HEC films are possible when the HEC is first modified (insolubilized) by reactions that cross-link the polymer chains. This is usually done by the reaction of a polyfunctional compound with the available hydroxyl groups in the polymer. Effective reactants include dialdehydes (such as glyoxal, glutaraldehyde, and 2-hydroxyadipaldehyde), dimethylol urea, and water-soluble urea- and melamine-formaldehyde resins. Almost any degree of water insolubility may be obtained.

A suggested formulation is:

Component	Parts by Weight
HEC	5
Glyoxal, 40%	12 as supplied
Water	83

Films laid down from this mixture and heated to 105C until dry are clear and glossy. They will resist up to one hour's soaking in water at room temperature before softening.

To produce films that are insoluble in boiling water, 0.15 part of aluminum sulfate is added to the above formulation, and the dried film is cured at 160C for one minute.

In addition to their compatibility with plasticizers, films of HEC can be modified with various natural gums and synethetic resins to change their properties. A list of the gums and resins compatible with HEC in film is given in Table 4.11.

TABLE 4.11 Gums and resins compatible with hydroxyethylcellulose in films.

Compatible	
Dextrin	Gum Tragacanth
Borated Dextrin	Sodium Alginate
Gum Arabic	Sodium Carboxymethyl–
Gum Karaya	Cellulose
Partly Compatible	
Casein	Methyl Cellulose
Gelatin	Starch
Polyvinyl Alcohol	
Incompatible	
Zein	

Properties of HEC Films

Films of HEC are relatively insoluble in most organic solvents. They will, however, dissolve in dimethyl sulfoxide, dimethylformamide, and dimethyl-acetamide. They retain their clarity and do not yellow even after 20-year storage at room temperature. The HEC films are highly resistant to animal, vegetable, and mineral oils and greases.

HEC films will discolor when heated in excess of 100C for a prolonged period; or they will begin to char at about 200C after a fast warm-up. At even higher temperatures, more extensive decomposition and melting takes place concurrently.

Adhesion of HEC films to glass, metal, fiber, and other surfaces can be improved by adding small amounts of either soybean glue or caustic to the solution of HEC before filming.

The hardness of all grades of HEC is about equal. At higher relative humidities, low-viscosity grades produce films that appear to remain slightly harder than those produced from high-viscosity grades. Any film made from a cellulosic will become somewhat softened at higher relative humidities, where the plasticizing effect of moisture becomes more noticeable.

HEC, like unmodified cellulose, is hygroscopic. Films made from it resist build-up of electrostatic charges, even at low humidities. Data on the moisture desorption and absorption properties of HEC is shown in Figures 4.10 and 4.11.

Films of HEC can be made photosensitive by the action of chromates and some diazo compounds. Subsequent exposure to ultraviolet light temporarily insolubilizes the exposed areas. The following formula is a starting point in the preparation of a photosensitive coating.

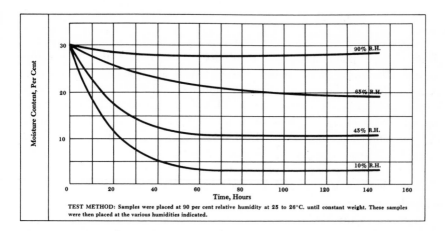

FIGURE 4.10   Desorption of water from moist Cellosize hydroxyethyl-cellulose.

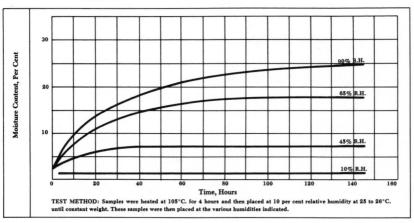

FIGURE 4.11   Absorption of water in dried Cellosize hydroxyethyl-cellulose.

TEST METHOD: Samples were heated at 105C for 4 hours and then placed at 10 per cent relative humidity at 25–26C until constant weight. These samples were then placed at the various humidities indicated.

Component	Parts by Weight
HEC, low-viscosity type	10.00
Ammonium bichromate	2.5
Ammonia, 28%	0.5
Water	240.0
	253.0

GENERAL

Hydroxyethylcellulose has many diverse uses and applications practically all of which depend first on its solubility in water, and also no less importantly on some of the other characteristics described in this chapter. Many of these applications have been identified and developed by the users in order to fill otherwise unmet needs. This type of growth will undoubtedly continue in the future. Both of the domestic HEC manufacturers have large and competent technical staffs which are studying HEC, its properties and its uses. These staffs cannot anticipate all potential applications where its unique properties would make HEC especially beneficial. They can however combine their knowledge of HEC with that of customers in working out many developments.

Thus is appears that almost any industrial or commercial process or product that involves the presence of water or a predominantly aqueous liquid could benefit in some manner by the use of HEC, and further, technology exists to exploit these possibilities.

ACKNOWLEDGMENT

All tables and graphs in this chapter are reproduced with the permission of Union Carbide Corporation.

George S. Baird
John K. Speicher

Hercules Inc.
Wilmington, Delaware

5

Carboxymethylcellulose

Carboxymethylcellulose is a water-soluble gum which, in a purified state, is designated as cellulose gum. Many applications of cellulose gum follow the pattern set by naturally occurring vegetable gums. Although cellulose gum may be considered as a plastic that is softened by water and hardened by removing water, and although it will form solid plastic masses or transparent films, many of its commercial uses depend as much on the characteristics of aqueous solutions as on the physical properties of the solid gum. Before discussing the applications in detail, the constitution and properties of carboxymethylcellulose should be considered, for its uses all stem from some specific property or combination of properties.

CHEMISTRY OF CMC

Commercially, carboxymethylcellulose is sold as the sodium salt, and to be scientifically precise should be called sodium carboxymethylcellulose. However, it has become fairly well-established trade practice to call the commercial product carboxymethylcellulose, or CMC, and on those rare occasions when the acid is referred to, to call it CMC free acid. An older name, found in the literature but no longer used commercially, is sodium cellulose glycolate. In this chapter the term CMC will be used, except when referring specifically to the highly purified material which is more properly called cellulose gum.

The basic manufacturing process consists of impregnating cellulose with sodium hydroxide to form alkali cellulose and then causing the alkali cellulose to react with monochloroacetic acid or sodium monochloroacetate to produce sodium carboxymethylcellulose. The principal by-product is sodium chloride. Neutralizing and drying the reaction mass yields crude CMC which contains considerable sodium chloride but is adequate for some technical applications. Washing the reaction mass with an alcohol-water mixture properly proportioned will extract salt and other by-products without dissolving the CMC.

Cellulose $(C_6H_{10}O_5)_x$ is a straight-chain polymer of vegetable origin. In plant growth, the conversion of carbon dioxide and water into starches and sugars and finally into cellulose involves many complexities. Here it will suffice to consider that cellulose is obtained from glucose, $C_6H_{12}O_6$, by the loss of one molecule of water from each glucose unit. The repeating unit in a cellulose chain is therefore anhydroglucose, $C_6H_{10}O_5$, and each anhydroglucose unit has three hydroxyl (OH) groups, as the following indicates:

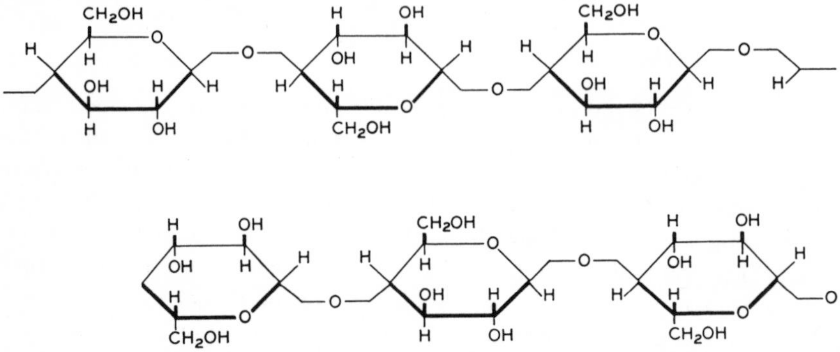

These hydroxyl groups are responsible for making cellulose such a valuable raw material for chemical modification. Spaced at regular intervals along the polymer chain, the hydroxyl groups are subject to esterification or etherification in whole or in part. In the case of CMC, the reaction is an etherification in which the carboxymethyl group (—CH₂COOH) is attached to the cellulose (R) through an ether linkage, R—O—CH₂COOH. Since the reaction is carried out in an alkaline medium, the product is the sodium salt of the carboxylic acid, R—O—CH₂COONa. The reaction of cellulose with sodium hydroxide to form alkali cellulose may be shown as:

$$ROH \ + \ NaOH \ \rightarrow \ RONa \ + \ H_2O$$

The reaction of alkali cellulose with sodium monochloroacetate can be shown as:

$$RONa \ + \ ClCH_2COONa \ \rightarrow \ ROCH_2COONa \ + \ NaCl$$

The reactions shown here involve one hydroxyl group, although there are actually three hydroxyl groups on each anhydroglucose unit in a cellulose polymer chain; and there may be several thousand hydroxyl groups on one chain, the exact number depending on the length of the particular chain.

These hydroxyl groups may be carboxymethylated to any desired extent; the extent of the reaction is referred to as degree of substitution, or DS. Since there are three hydroxyls per anhydroglucose unit, complete substitution is designated as a DS of 3. Carboxymethylcellulose of quite low DS (approximately 0.2 to 0.3) is soluble in aqueous alkali. As the DS is increased, CMC becomes increasingly water-soluble. Commercial types of CMC are usually within the DS range of 0.50 to 0.85, but may vary from 0.4 to 1.5.

Solubility in water and, more particularly, the characteristics of the solutions obtained depend not only on DS but also on the uniformity of distribution of the substituent carboxymethyl groups along the polymer chain. The more uniform the distribution the smoother and less thixotropic the solutions will be.

Degree of polymerization, DP, also affects the properties of cellulose derivatives. Because the polymer chains of cellulose vary in length, the average degree of polymerization is usually given. Generally, cellulose products of high average DP have better film strength properties than those of lower average DP.

In the case of CMC, the most important aspect of average DP is its relation to the viscosity of solutions. When CMC of high average DP is dissolved in water, it produces solutions of high viscosity. As the average DP decreases, so does the solution viscosity. Because of this property, CMC is often used to control or to increase viscosity.

Combinations and permutations of the three chemical variables described, namely, degree of substitution, uniformity of substitution, and degree of polymerization, afford a wide variety of types of CMC. Another variable is purity, which may range from crude CMC containing a high proportion of sodium chloride to a product assaying 99.5+ per cent CMC.

Purely physical characteristics, such as particle size and shape, and particle density, also can be varied over a considerable range by manufacturing procedures. Taking all of these possibilities into consideration, it is obvious that special types and grades of CMC can be produced to meet the special requirements of many different specific industrial applications.

In this connection, the highly purified CMC, cellulose gum, which is sold for use in foods, pharmaceuticals, and cosmetics, may vary only within limits prescribed by applicable standards, such as the United States Pharmacopeia, the standards of the Toilet Goods Association, etc.

CMC, manufactured in a highly alkaline medium, is quite stable when stored or used in alkaline surroundings if oxygen is excluded. Any change in the characteristics of CMC that may occur on storage or use under adverse conditions is usually a decrease in viscosity, caused by a decrease in DP.

In highly acid conditions, depolymerization is hydrolytic in character. Under highly alkaline conditions in the presence of oxygen an oxidative degradation may occur. Optimum storage conditions are at a pH of 7.0 to 9.0, in the absence of oxygen and sunlight, and at moderate temperature. Freezing has no permanent effect on the viscosity of CMC solutions.

The viscosity of CMC solutions decreases and increases, reversibly, with raising and lowering of temperature, but no permanent change occurs unless the solutions are kept at high temperatures for a considerable time. For instance, the solutions may be heated to boiling for a few minutes or stored at 70 to 80C for 24 hours with only a minor loss of viscosity.

CMC is somewhat more resistant to biological attack than are other water-soluble gums. If CMC solutions are to be stored under conditions favoring mold or fungus growth, the addition of a preservative is advisable. Many of the commonly used mold inhibitors are effective with CMC, and the inhibitor which best fits the requirements and limitations of the end product should be chosen. The first indication of biological attack is usually an otherwise unaccounted for decrease in solution viscosity.

Another influence effecting a chemical change in CMC is that of alkalies, acids, and salts on CMC solutions. As stated previously, some types of CMC of low DS that are not water-soluble are soluble in aqueous alkali. Even the best water-soluble types are more completely dispersed, as evidenced by lower viscosity, in solutions at a pH of 10 to 12. This is particularly noticeable with the higher viscosity types.

The behavior of CMC under acid conditions depends to some extent on the acid involved and to a larger extent on the pH. When a CMC solution is acidified with strong mineral acids, the sodium salt is converted to the free acid form, which is water-insoluble, and precipitates. This precipitation may occur at a pH of 2 to 3, depending on the acid used and the DS of the CMC. Types with a DS of 0.7 will precipitate at a slightly higher pH than will types with a DS of 1.2. Weak organic acids in moderate amounts have no important effect on CMC.

Although CMC free acid is water-insoluble, there is a phenomenon by which such a solution can be obtained. If a solution of CMC (sodium salt) is passed through a bed of ion-exchange resin that replaces sodium ions with hydrogen ions, the CMC free acid formed remains in solution. If this solution is evaporated to dryness, the solid CMC free acid remaining is water-insoluble.

The effect of salts on CMC solutions depends on the particular salt. Solution compatibility is quite good with salts that form a soluble salt of CMC, such as sodium and potassium salts. Calcium chloride added to a CMC solution will produce a haze but no definite precipitate. A soluble ferric or aluminum salt will produce either a precipitate or a solid gel. As a rough guide, monovalent cations will generally form soluble salts of CMC, divalent cations are borderline, and trivalent cations form insoluble products. There are other more complex interactions of ionizing salts which may lead to incompatibility or viscosity changes.

The formation of CMC gels by means of polyvalent cations may be utilized for controlled gelation. For example, colorless solid gels which are stable indefinitely when preserved against bacterial attack, and which are composed of as much as 98 per cent water, can be prepared by treating CMC solutions with aluminum salts.

PHYSICAL CHARACTERISTICS OF CMC

Commercial CMC is a solid granular material which may vary from coarse granules to a rather fine powder, depending on the source, grade, and type. CMC tends to absorb and hold moisture and some of its large-volume uses hinge on this water-binding ability. As an illustration of this ability, one common type of CMC at 77F and 50 per cent relative humidity has an equilibrium content of about 18 per cent.

By evaporating the water from CMC solutions, clear sheets or films may be formed which are quite strong and fairly flexible, as indicated by the test data in Table 5.1.

TABLE 5.1.   Properties of Typical Samples of Unplasticized CMC Film.

| | Typical Property Value | | |
Property Tested	CMC-7L*	CMC-7M	CMC-7H
Tensile strength, psi	8,300	13,000	15,000
Elongation, per cent at break	8.3	14.3	14.3
Flexibility, MIT double folds	93	131	513
Electrostatic charge	negative	negative	negative
Refractive index	1.515	1.515	1.515
Specific gravity	1.59	1.59	1.59

* The figure 7 as used here is Hercules' designation for a type of CMC having a DS of approximately 0.7. The letters L, M and H designate low, medium and high viscosity grades, respectively.

Although CMC is designed to be soluble in water and insoluble in organic solvents, aqueous solutions of CMC will tolerate considerable quantities of water-miscible organic solvents, such as ethanol or acetone. The tolerance of several CMC solutions for ethanol is shown in Table 5.2.

CMC is compatible with water-soluble gums and polymers, such as gum arabic, gum tragacanth, locust bean gum, casein, starch, gelatin, pectin, Irish moss, sodium alginate, sodium silicate, and many others. CMC is also compatible with glycerol, various glycols, and derivatives of both.

TABLE 5.2.   Tolerance of CMC Solutions for Ethanol.

CMC Viscosity Type	Volume Ratio of Ethanol * to CMC Solution (1 per cent)	
	First Evident Haze	First Distinct Precipitate
CMC-7 Low (7L)	2.4–1	3.6–1
CMC-7 Medium (7M)	2.1–1	2.7–1
CMC-7 High (7H)	1.6–1	1.6–1

* The ethanol (95 per cent) was added slowly, at room temperature, to the vigorously stirred CMC solution.

CMC is soluble in either hot or cold water. Solutions of CMC are prepared by merely stirring the dry granular material into water. The rate of adding the CMC and the amount of agitation should be regulated so that no large lumps of partially dissolved material form. If lumps do form, either by too rapid addition of the CMC or by inadequate stirring, the time of solution will be greatly prolonged.

CMC may be dry-blended with other dry ingredients that are to be added to water subsequently to make a solution, paste, dough, or other finished composition. Ease of solution is one of the advantageous properties of CMC.

The wide variation in solution viscosity that can be obtained by choice of CMC type and concentration is illustrated in Figure 5.1. To obtain a high-viscosity solution with a minimum concentration of CMC a high-viscosity type is used; and vice versa, to obtain maximum concentration at a reasonably low-solution viscosity a low-viscosity type is used. With the highest viscosity type shown on the graph a 2 per cent solution has a viscosity of about 50,000 centipoises (500 poises), a viscosity that might be described as "heavy enough to walk on." In contrast, with the lowest viscosity type a 2 per cent solution has a viscosity between 10 and 20 centipoises.

CMC solutions are non-Newtonian liquids but are pseudoplastic, i.e., in a viscosity determination the rate of shear is not directly proportional to the shearing stress applied, and the apparent viscosity obtained depends on the method of testing. Manufacturers of CMC use highly standardized methods for measuring the viscosity of their products; if a different method is employed, the results will not agree.

In addition to being pseudoplastic, CMC solutions may or may not be thixotropic, depending on the procedure used in making the CMC. A thixotropic CMC solution will increase in apparent viscosity on standing, in some cases even develop a gel structure, and then revert to its original apparent viscosity when agitated or caused to flow. In certain applications

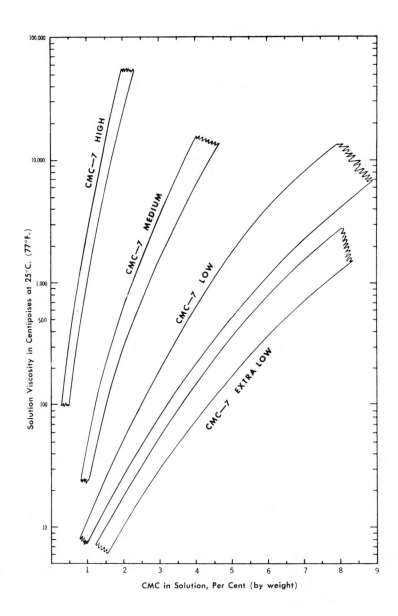

FIGURE 5.1 Viscosity-concentration curves for four viscosity types of CMC.

of CMC, discussed later in this chapter, thixotropic solutions are undesirable, while in others thixotropy is essential.

PHYSIOLOGICAL PROPERTIES OF CELLULOSE GUM

Extensive investigations have been made on the physiological properties of cellulose gum, including feeding studies with rats, guinea pigs, dogs, and humans; metabolism studies; patch test programs; and topical use. All of these studies have indicated that on oral ingestion, cellulose gum is physiologically inert. A similar conclusion has been reached regarding skin exposure.

APPLICATIONS OF CMC

The discussion up to this point has omitted much detail concerning the chemical, physical, and physiological properties of CMC, and some of the details not mentioned have a bearing on specific uses of CMC. Enough has been said, however, to elucidate the principal characteristics of CMC and the possibilities of utilizing its functional properties in commercial applications.

CMC is a colloid, readily soluble in water, insoluble in organic materials and, therefore, resistant to oils and greases, physiologically inert, anionic in character, and is an efficient viscosity (or consistency) control agent.

As with many other materials, a method of manufacturing CMC was known for some years before any significant place was found for CMC in commerce and industry. Utilization of CMC started during the controlled economy of the pre-World War II effort of Germany to become self-sufficient, and developed further with wartime material shortages. Its primary pre-war use was as an adhesive to replace starch, which was being conserved for food use. Its wartime use was in synthetic detergents to reduce fat requirements in soap manufacturing.

The earliest known commercial interest in CMC in the United States was that of Hercules Inc. in the years just before the war. Development was handicapped during the war, but shortly after the close of the war Hercules placed a CMC plant into production, using a new process which yielded a product far superior to the German material. The introduction of CMC to the American market at that time was opportune, for world markets in gums were badly disrupted and supplies of imported natural gums were uncertain.

At the present time in the United States, CMC is produced for sale by E. I. du Pont de Nemours & Company, Hercules Inc., Wyandotte Chemical Company and Warner Chemical Co., and for captive use by the Buckeye

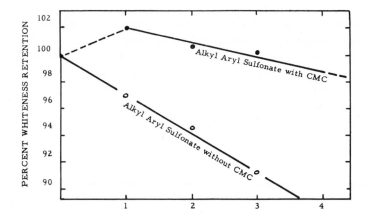

FIGURE 5.2 Synthetic detergent laundry solutions give better whiteness when they contain CMC. The difference becomes more pronounced if the same wash water is used for several loads.

Cellulose Corporation. In Canada, it is made for sale by Chemical Developments of Canada Ltd.

Detergents and Soaps

The use of CMC in detergents, which first led to large-volume production,
has continued to grow and today the detergent industry is the largest consumer of CMC in the world. Synthetic detergents do an excellent job of
loosening soil in laundering operations, but do not have the ability to keep
the loosened soil completely suspended throughout the operation. Hence if
detergents are used without a soil-suspending agent, some of the soil is re-
deposited on the clothing or other materials being washed. The addition of
as little as 0.3 to 1.0 per cent of CMC to synthetic detergent formulations
overcomes this difficulty. In Figure 5.2 the whiteness retention is plotted
against the number of laundry loads washed in the same solutions using a
typical detergent without any soil-suspending agent, and, in comparison,
the same detergent with CMC added. The improved performance of the
detergent when compounded with CMC is quite evident.

Soap has good soil-suspending properties, but when the detergency of
soap is improved by adding inorganic alkaline materials (as is done in
"built" soaps) the soil-suspending ability is decreased. Here again CMC
proves advantageous. By adding 2 to 5 per cent CMC (based on the weight
of builder), the improved detergency of the built formulation is retained and
redeposition of soil avoided.

In explanation of the rather remarkable ability of very small percentages of CMC to prevent redeposition of soil, it has been shown by laboratory investigations that CMC is selectively absorbed by cotton fibers by hydrogen bonding. A negative charge is introduced by the carboxymethyl group which repels the negatively charged dirt particles, thus preventing them from reattaching to the fiber.

Technical grades of CMC are usually suitable for detergent use; purified grades may be used where the presence of sodium chloride would be objectionable. Most CMC used in detergents and built soaps is added by the manufacturer or compounder, but CMC is also used directly in commercial and home laundries, either for soil suspension or for other effects such as sizing material.

Fabric Sizes

The soil-repelling property of CMC, as evidenced by its effectiveness in preventing soil redeposition during laundering, suggests the possibility that a fabric sized with CMC should be more soil resistant than either an unsized fabric or one sized with a more conventional sizing material. An extensive testing program, carried out some years ago at the Institute of Textile Technology at Charlottesville, Virginia, demonstrated that this was the case. CMC-treated fabrics were found to be resistant to soiling and easy to wash clean. It was also demonstrated that a fabric sized with CMC has a relatively soft but crisp hand and has good crease resistance.

Commercial utilization of this information has proceeded along several lines. CMC is used in commercial laundries by adding small quantities in the final sour or bluing operation. The result is a high-quality finish providing bright sparkling whites and sharp colors. Ironability is improved as well as soil resistance. CMC is also used in regular starching work by replacing 10 per cent of the starch with CMC to improve ironability and application properties of the starch. CMC is marketed as a liquid starch for home use and is a component in some conventional starch formulations.

The soft but crisp finish imparted by CMC may be utilized in dry-cleaning operations to resize wet-cleaned garments in the final rinse.

Textile Manufacture

A quite different kind of sizing from that associated with laundering is the warp size used by textile mills. The use of CMC as a warp size involves several characteristic properties of the material and is an excellent example of the premise previously expressed, that applications of CMC stem logically from its physical, chemical, and biological properties.

The combination of properties responsible for the use of CMC in warp sizing are these: rapid and easy solubility in water; water-binding ability; the considerable physical strength and toughness of the dry film produced on evaporating a solution; resistance, but not complete immunity, to biological attack.

The reasons these properties are advantageous in warp sizing should be obvious. Ease of solution is, of course, desirable in making up the size mixture, but is of much greater import in removing the size after weaving. With a material that is not readily and completely water-soluble, desizing is difficult. The water-binding ability of CMC makes high humidity in the weaving area less critical than with some other sizes. Lower humidity not only in-

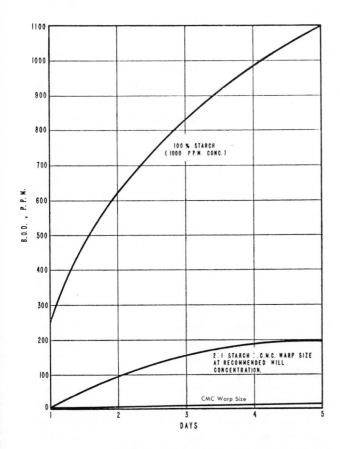

FIGURE 5.3 B.O.D. exerted by 100 per cent starch sizing as compared to B.O.D. exerted by CMC warp size, and by 2:1 starch: CMC warp-size blend at comparable use levels.

creases comfort but also makes maintenance less costly. The toughness of the coating on the yarn controls shedding; the stronger the coating the less shedding of both size and fiber. The waste from desizing frequently causes stream pollution problems which are less severe if the size is relatively resistant to biological attack.

This last observation deserves some further comment. Organic materials that appear to be innocuous may be highly objectionable stream pollutants if, in the process of decomposition, they deplete the water of free oxygen and thus kill the fish. The rate of consumption of oxygen by decomposition of organic matter is measured as biological oxygen demand (B.O.D.). The B.O.D. exerted by CMC is very low in comparison with starch, as shown in Figure 5.3. Furthermore, the B.O.D. of a CMC-starch mixture is lower than one would predict from a weighted average.

As industry becomes increasingly conscious of its civic responsibilities, many companies are making sincere (and costly) efforts to avoid stream pollution. The low B.O.D. of CMC, therefore, becomes a matter of first-rank interest in any use, such as warp sizing, in which the material becomes waste after serving its intended purpose.

Printing is another step in textile processing which uses CMC. Printing pastes thickened with CMC give sharp outlines, the dried prints are soft, and the gum washes out easily. Solutions are readily prepared and are not sensitive to acids and alkalies within the pH range used in textile printing. A newer system of printing involves incorporating the dye and necessary chemicals into an emulsion system containing a petroleum solvent. Purified types of CMC are used to stabilize the emulsion and to regulate viscosity.

Other textile applications of CMC are backsizing, pigment binding, as a binder for nonwoven fabrics, and as a relatively permanent finish when insolubilized.

Paper and Paper Products

Consideration of CMC in textile sizing leads logically to its consideration in paper sizing. There are many ways in which CMC is used or might be used in or on the many kinds of paper which exist.

One of the first uses of CMC as a paper size, and still an important one, was the application of CMC to boxboard at the calender stack. Once upon a time shipping cases were purely utilitarian with essential information about the contents stencilled on. Today paperboard-shipping cases are better than ever functionally, and are also an advertising medium which shows the contents, the manufacturer's name and trademark, and other information in large bold letters. Sometimes almost the entire surface is covered with ink; thus a good surface on which to print is imperative.

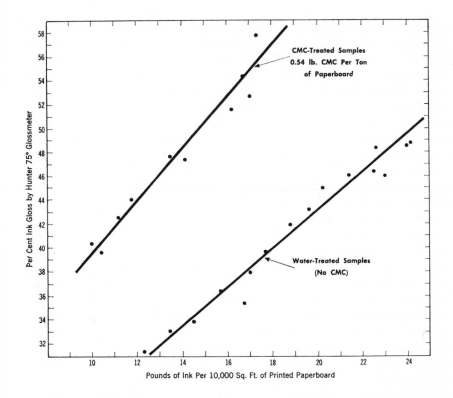

FIGURE 5.4   Ink gloss, plotted against quantity of ink used, on paper-board calender sized with CMC, as compared to the same board without CMC. Note reduction in ink required at all levels of gloss.

The film-forming ability of CMC is useful in this situation. Quite small amounts of CMC, applied as a calender size, form a sufficiently impervious film or coating on the surface of the board to prevent undue penetration of ink. The result is a saving in ink and a more attractive product. In Figure 5.4 the improvement in gloss at any given spread of ink, or the saving in ink at any given level of gloss, is shown graphically.

A similar saving can be made when paper or board is waxed. A very little CMC on the surface will decrease wax penetration.

A surface size of CMC can also be obtained by size-press application. A CMC coating so applied lowers the porosity of the sheet, improves grease and oil resistance, increases the dry strength, and improves smoothness. CMC is sometimes used in combination with a surface size of starch to control the degree of penetration of the starch. For most surface-sizing operations, whether applied at the size press or at the calender, the use of a well-purified grade of CMC is advisable.

Recently a new type of CMC (of lower DS than most commercial types) has appeared, designed specifically as an internal additive, or beater size, for paper. The bonding of one cellulose fiber to another to produce a fairly strong structure, as occurs in papermaking, is a complex subject; but it is a generally accepted theory that hydrogen bonding is important in the procedure. Introducing small quantities of CMC of controlled solubility into the paper pulp during beating promotes fiber bonding and produces a stronger, more rigid structure. Autoradiographs and electron photomicrographs show the internal additive to be present as a more or less uniform coating over the fiber surfaces, thus making increased interfiber bonding possible at all points of contact.

Adhesives

As already stated, the earliest use of CMC in any appreciable quantity was as an adhesive. The quality of adhesiveness, i.e., the capability of binding things together, is a factor in many of the applications of CMC; but its use purely as an adhesive is limited because there are lower cost water-soluble materials adequate for many adhesive uses.

Perhaps the best example of a CMC adhesive is wallpaper paste. A CMC solution does not have the wet tack or quick tack frequently desired in adhesives. In wallpaper paste, the absence of quick tack is an advantage because time is needed to adjust the paper and move it into exact position before it becomes immobile. CMC as a wallpaper paste also meets the requirements of a nonstaining paste.

Emulsions, Latexes, and Dispersions

CMC finds numerous applications resulting from, or related to, the property of increasing the consistency or body of aqueous mixtures, that is, its ability to adjust and control viscosity. Suspensions of finely divided solids in water, which would normally settle out, may be stabilized by incorporating CMC. Similarly, emulsions and latexes may also be stabilized.

Complex mixtures, such as the emulsion or latex paints, illustrate this use of CMC. In latex paints, the vehicle is a latex made by the emulsion polymerization of styrene-butadiene, of vinyl acetate, of an acrylate ester, etc. High percentages of pigment are suspended in the vehicles, and various modifying agents added in smaller amounts. The resulting complex mixture must have uniform consistency and flow properties from lot to lot; it must be able to withstand sudden and extreme temperature changes and vibration during storage and shipment. Finally, when used the paint should brush easily and flow out well, but not sag.

CMC, used as the stabilizer in such paints, greatly aids in achieving the balance of properties needed. A rather pure grade of CMC is required for this use since salt or other contaminant would be deleterious. In addition, a CMC which is not thixotropic and which gives very smooth, nongranular solutions is usually preferred.

Oil Well-Drilling Fluids

Drilling fluid, more commonly called mud, is another example of the use of CMC to stabilize a suspension — in this case, a suspension of heavy solid materials in water.

In drilling oil wells with a rotary drill, it is necessary to pump a fluid down the drill pipe, which fluid then circulates through the drill bit and back up the casing, carrying the cuttings with it. Drilling mud has several functions beyond the primary one of removing cuttings: it cools and lubricates the bit; it coats the wall of the hole, thus preventing loss of fluid to the formations drilled through; it prevents ingress of liquids and gases; and it aids in preventing unconsolidated formations from caving into the hole.

Drilling muds are basically aqueous dispersions of clay or bentonite and weighting agents, such as barite. A colloidal thickener must, of course, be included to prevent settling, and CMC is ideal for the purpose. One of the advantageous properties of CMC in this use is that the solution is not affected by salt (salt water is encountered in many drilling operations); another is the stability of CMC at the high temperatures encountered in deep wells. In drilling mud CMC which tends to be thixotropic is preferred.

Miscellaneous Industrial Uses of CMC

The suspending and binding properties of CMC are used in the ceramics industry. It is used as a green strength binder and is completely burnt out during firing. Among the current ceramic applications are use in sanitary-ware glazes, structural tile glazes, refractories, glaze binder and jigger-body additive in dinnerware, and as a binder and suspending agent in vitreous enamels.

CMC is used as a desensitizer in preparing lithographic plates. Its use here depends on the fact that a CMC coating is very water receptive and very ink repellent.

CMC is used in foundry work as a core binder. It is also used in insecticide formulations to stabilize emulsions, to suspend solids, and as a "sticker" to bind the insecticide to plant leaves.

A great many other miscellaneous uses could be listed but perhaps these are enough to indicate the wide range of industrial applications.

APPLICATIONS OF CELLULOSE GUM

Some of the applications for CMC that have been discussed need a high-grade, well-purified material; others have less stringent requirements. For instance, the CMC used to stabilize a delicately balanced emulsion system needs to be free of salt or other by-products, whereas the CMC used in a household detergent need not be of such high purity. In these industrial applications, there is some choice from which the best-suited quality of CMC can be selected. Applications for personal consumption, such as foods, pharmaceuticals, and cosmetics, however, require purified grades of CMC that meet applicable standards.

As already stated, pure CMC, suitable for use in foods, pharmaceuticals, etc., is designated cellulose gum. It should be understood that although there are limits of purity imposed on cellulose gum, there remain allowable differences in viscosity, particle size, particle density, and solution properties.

Food

The properties that make cellulose gum a useful material in food products can be explained best by examples of such use. Ice cream is a good example since this was one of the early uses of cellulose gum in food.

In ice cream and sherbets, cellulose gum functions as a stabilizer to inhibit growth of ice crystals. Figure 5.5 illustrates the effectiveness of a cellulose gum stabilizer used at less than 0.2 per cent by weight of the ice cream mix. The resulting ice cream has a good smooth texture, is relatively resistant to heat shock, and maintains its desirable texture on aging.

Cellulose gum also acts as a stabilizer to inhibit crystal growth in sugar systems. Added to icings, toppings, and glazes, it preserves initial smoothness and prevents water loss.

In products containing starch, cellulose gum tends to prevent syneresis. The gel properties of food hydrocolloids, such as pectin and gelatin, may be modified by the inclusion of cellulose gum.

Cellulose gum serves as an emulsion stabilizer in salad dressings; it controls consistency in cheese spreads; it gives better control of grease holdout and better shelf life in doughnuts. Dried dairy products which must be reconstituted are much easier to rehydrate if some cellulose gum is added before dehydration. Cellulose gum will efficiently thicken dietetic foods without adding to the calorie content.

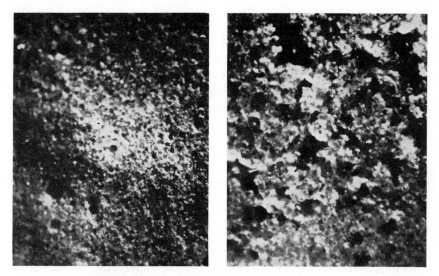

FIGURE 5.5 Effect of cellulose gum stabilizer on ice crystal growth in ice cream. Photographed at 38× after two weeks' storage at 5 to 8F. (Control sample at right, cellulose gum stabilized sample at left.)

Pharmaceuticals

Cellulose gum is used in pharmaceutical preparations in much the same way that water-soluble gums have been used for many years, that is, as a thickener, suspending agent, and film-former. The uniformity, physiological inertness, availability, and price stability of cellulose gum are of advantage in this field, as in others.

Thixotropic, high-viscosity types of cellulose gum are excellent suspending agents for such products as calamine lotion, or the barium sulfate suspensions used in X-ray diagnostic work.

Cellulose gum gels serve as carriers for medicinals for external application, such as jellies, salves, or ointments. Cellulose gum solutions may be used with flavors to replace the sugar syrups frequently used to thicken pharmaceutical preparations. Cellulose gum also is used as a binder in the manufacture of tablets.

In addition to the uses listed, and others in which cellulose gum is a mechanical or physical aid to the use or application of a medicament, cellulose gum finds use as a bulk laxative because of its water-holding characteristic. It reaches maximum hydration under the alkaline conditions found in the intestine. The cellulose gum may be tableted, or may be used in solution as a liquid bulk laxative.

Cosmetics

The same principles used in formulating pharmaceutical preparations for external use apply to cosmetics such as lotions and hand creams, in which cellulose gum is used as an emollient, thickener, and emulsion stabilizer. The soil-suspending properties of cellulose gum are applicable to shampoo formulations, and in bubble-bath formulations cellulose gum also acts as a foam stabilizer.

Cellulose gum is used as a viscosity control agent, dispersant, and suspending agent in toothpaste. It is compatible with glycerol and the detergent components of toothpaste, and good viscosity control is obtained from batch to batch.

SUMMARY

Accurate current statistics are not available for the consumption of CMC, either in specific markets or in total. It is known that U.S. production in 1947 was of the order of 2 million pounds, and that by 1956 this had increased to about 25 million pounds. It is estimated that this rate of growth has continued to date.

As stated previously, on a worldwide basis the use of CMC in combination with synthetic detergents is presumed to be the largest outlet for the material. As detergents continue to displace soap this market will probably grow.

The advent of the pure CMC, cellulose gum, opened not only the food and pharmaceutical markets, but also numerous industrial markets which required better quality than a technical CMC, and these markets have a healthy growth potential.

The broadly diversified pattern of CMC applications that has developed in a relatively brief history gives promise of further diversification and broader fields of use.

The basic raw material, cellulose, is readily available; thus the problem of inadequate supply should not arise, even if uses of CMC multiply beyond present horizons.

Note: All charts and tables in this chapter are reproduced with the permission of Hercules Inc.

C. P. Argana
E. P. Czerwin

Electrochemicals Department
E. I. du Pont de Nemours & Company
Wilmington, Delaware

6

Polyvinyl Alcohol

Polyvinyl alcohol, first synthesized in Germany in 1925, was commercially introduced in the United States by the Du Pont Company in 1939. A combination of unique product properties found only ln polyvinyl alcohol makes it one of the most versatile water-soluble resins available to industry.

Chemically, polyvinyl alcohol can be classified broadly as a polyhydric alcohol with secondary hydroxyl groups on alternate carbon atoms. As is true with most polymeric materials, variations in structure or composition can have a profound effect on end-use characteristics, thereby making the polymer more adaptable to some applications than to others. In the case of polyvinyl alcohol, changes in product properties — thus changes in application utility — can be controlled in the manufacturing process as well as by chemical modification or compounding at the time of use.

MANUFACTURE

In producing polyvinyl alcohol resin a multistep process is used since vinyl alcohol monomer is a nonexistent entity, rapidly rearranging itself into acetaldehyde. Thus, it is first necessary to produce polyvinyl acetate resin from vinyl acetate monomer, and follow with alcoholysis of the polyvinyl acetate to the polyvinyl alcohol.

These reactions are illustrated as follows:

$$CH{=}CH_2 \quad \xrightarrow[\text{Catalyst}]{\text{Heat}} \quad \left[\begin{array}{c} -CH{-}CH_2 \\ | \\ OCOCH_3 \end{array} \right]_x \quad \xrightarrow{\text{Catalyst}} \quad \begin{array}{c} -CH{-}CH_2{-}CH{-}CH_2{-} \\ | \qquad\qquad | \\ OH \qquad\quad OH \end{array}$$

Vinyl acetate   *Polyvinyl acetate*   *Polyvinyl alcohol*

Polymerization of the vinyl acetate resin is carried out by conventional processing techniques, using either bulk or bead polymerization. The resulting polyvinyl acetate resin is then dissolved in a solvent, usually methanol,

109

and alcoholized by use of either an acid or alkaline catalyst. Polyvinyl alcohol, insoluble in the methanol and by-product methyl acetate, precipitates out and is then filtered, washed, dried, and packaged. The polyvinyl alcohol is characterized by the viscosity or degree of polymerization and the per cent alcoholysis or degree of saponification.

Both viscosity and alcoholysis are controlled in the manufacturing process and are important in determining end-product characteristics and commercial utility. The molecular weight, or measure of polymer viscosity, is a direct function of the molecular weight of the precursive polyvinyl acetate resin fed to the alcoholysis reaction. This is normally controlled by use of "chain-breakers" during the polyvinyl acetate polymerization.

Generally speaking, polyvinyl alcohol is commercially available in four molecular weight ranges. For simplicity in discussing molecular weight or degree of polymerization, the four types are referred to as super-high, high-, medium-, and low-viscosity polyvinyl alcohols. The average molecular weights of the four types are: super-high viscosity, 250,000 to 300,000; high-viscosity 170,000 to 220,000; medium-viscosity, 120,000 to 150,000, and low-viscosity, 25,000 to 35,000.

As the molecular weight of polyvinyl alcohol decreases, the water sensitivity or ease of water solubility increases. Higher values for tensile strength, tear resistance, elongation, and flexibility are obtained with increasing molecular weight.

The per cent alcoholysis is controlled by either allowing the alcoholysis reaction to go to completion or stopping it at a desired level. Commercially, polyvinyl alcohols at two alcoholysis levels are considered important. These are the so-called partially hydrolyzed grades which represent products alcoholized 87 to 89 per cent and the completely hydrolyzed grades which are alcoholized 99 to 100 per cent.

Changes in per cent alcoholysis also affect product properties. As the per cent alcoholysis increases, tensile strength, tear resistance, and elongation increase. Water sensitivity is anomalous in that maximum sensitivity occurs at about 88 per cent alcoholysis. One would expect water sensitivity to increase further as complete alcoholysis is approached. However, as more hydroxyl groups replace acetyl groups from the polyvinyl acetate polymer, hydrogen bonding begins and water molecules find it increasingly difficult to envelop the polymer chain and effect solubility. Heat is therefore required to dissolve the completely alcoholized grades of polyvinyl alcohol. Use of heat also promotes solubility of the partially alcoholized grades.

By combining the variables of alcoholysis and viscosity, a range of polyvinyl alcohol types can be produced. For example, Du Pont produces eleven grades of Elvanol* polyvinyl alcohol which find commercial utility in large volume. End-use requirements govern selection of the grade used in any specific application.

The effects of viscosity and alcoholysis on the properties of polyvinyl alcohol are graphically summarized in Figure 6.1. The specifications of the grades of polyvinyl alcohol described in Figure 6.1 are given in Table 6.1

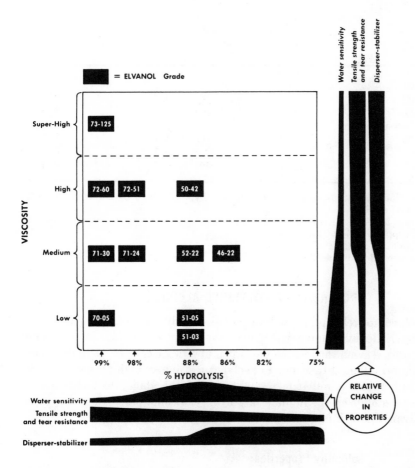

FIGURE 6.1   The effect of hydrolysis and viscosity on the properties of Du Pont's polyvinyl alcohol.

* Registered trademark of E. I. du Pont de Nemours & Company.

TABLE 6.1. Typical Polyvinyl Alcohol Specifications.[1]

Grade	Viscosity[2]	Per cent Hydrolysis	pH	Per cent Volatiles[3]	Per cent Ash[4]
Super-High Viscosity					
73–125	115–135	99.3–100	5–7	5	1.0
High-Viscosity					
72–60	55–65	99–100	5–7	5	1.0
72–51	45–55	97.6–98.4	5–7	5	1.0
50–42	35–45	87–89	5–7	5	0.75
Medium Viscosity					
71–30	28–32	99–100	5–7	5	1.0
71–24	23–22	97.6–98.4	5–7	5	1.0
52–22	21–25	87–89	5–7	5	0.75
46–22	21–25	84.7–86.8	5–7	5	0.75
Low-Viscosity					
71–05	4–6	99–100	5–7	5	1.0
51–05	4–6	88–89	5–7	5	0.75
51–03	1.8–3.0	88–89	5–7	5	0.75

[1] All specifications on dry basis except volatiles. Typical values for Du Pont Elvanol®
polyvinyl alcohol.
[2] Viscosity in centipoises of a 4 per cent water solution at 20C determined by means of
the Hoeppler falling ball method.
[3] Maximum.
[4] Maximum calculated as Na_2O.

PROPERTIES OF POLYVINYL ALCOHOL

Both completely and partially alcoholized polyvinyl alcohols have many
characteristics in common which make the polymer valuable to a number of
industries. Among the most important properties are: water solubility; ease
of film formation; grease, oil, and solvent resistance; high tensile strength;
excellent adhesive and binder qualities; and the ability to function as a
disperser-stabilizer. A summary of polyvinyl alcohol properties, as typified
by Elvanol polyvinyl alcohol, is given in Table 6.2.

Solubility Properties

With most polymers, water solubility warrants little further discussion.
In the case of polyvinyl alcohol, however, water solubility can vary over a
wide range — and with the variations comes versatility in end use. For
example, the water solubility of films or coatings can range from complete
solubility in a few seconds to relative insolubility over extended periods.
These differences depend on the type of polyvinyl alcohol employed. Com-

TABLE 6.2. Properties of Polyvinyl Alcohol.*

Form	Powder
Color	White to cream
Specific gravity	1.27–1.31
Specific volume, cu in./lb	22.9–21.1
Refractive index, $n_D{}^{25}$	1.49–1.53
Elongation, plasticized film, %	Up to 600
Tensile strength, dry, unplasticized, psi	Up to 22,000
Hardness, plasticized, Shore Durometer	10–100
Heat-sealing temperature, dry, unplasticized, °C	165–210
Compression-molding temperature, plasticized, °C	100–150
Heat stability, above 100C	Darkens slowly
above 150C	Darkens rapidly
above 200C	Decomposes
Storage stability (several years)	No deterioration
Thermal coefficient of linear expansion, 0 to 45°C	7×10^{-5} to 12×10^{-5}
Specific heat, cal/g/°C	0.4
Flammability	Burns at about rate of paper
Effect of light	Unaffected
Effect of strong acids	Dissolves or decomposes
Effect of strong alkalies	Softens or dissolves
Effect of weak acids	Softens or dissolves
Effect of weak alkalies	Softens or dissolves
Effect of organic solvents	Unaffected

* Values given for Du Pont's Elvanol polyvinyl alcohol.

pletely alcoholized grades are considered hot-water-soluble and cold-water-insoluble; partially alcoholized types are soluble in both hot and cold water. Thus, in adhesive formulations where water resistance is an important prerequisite, the completely alcoholized polyvinyl alcohols find most utility. Conversely, in remoistenable adhesives, where resolubility is important, partially alcoholized polyvinyl alcohols are used. Water solubility is also a function of molecular weight — the lower the molecular weight, the more readily soluble the polymer.

Water solutions of polyvinyl alcohol tolerate substantial amounts of such monohydric alcohols as methanol, ethanol, and isopropanol, the proportion increasing as the per cent hydrolysis of the contained polyvinyl alcohol decreases. For example, the maximum amount of isopropanol which can be present at room temperature, without causing part of the polyvinyl alcohol to precipitate, varies from about 40 per cent for Elvanol 72-60 to about 60 per cent for Elvanol 50-42.

Only a few types of organic compounds have any appreciable solvent action on the completely hydrolyzed grades of polyvinyl alcohol. Examples of these are some of the polyhydroxy compounds including glycerin, ethylene glycol, and a few of the lower polyethylene glycols; amines, including ethanolamines and ethanolamine salts; and amides, including formamide, ethanol formamide, and ethanol acetamide.

Solvent action on polyvinyl alcohol seems to be favored by hydroxyl, amino, and amide groups. Most of the solvents discussed require heat to dissolve even small amounts of polyvinyl alcohol. For example, polyvinyl alcohol can be dissolved in glycerin if heated to 120 to 150C; but the mixture gels when allowed to cool to room temperature. Diethylenetriamine and triethylenetetramine are among the few organic solvents which dissolve polyvinyl alcohol at room temperature.

Preparation of polyvinyl alcohol solutions is a relatively simple procedure. The recommended technique is to first slurry the polyvinyl alcohol powder into water at room temperature with good agitation. The resulting slurry is then heated to 190F or higher, until solution is complete, usually in 30 to 60 minutes. Agitation is continued during the heating cycle. Heat may be applied by injecting live steam into the solution make-up vessel or by means of a steam jacket or steam coil. Maximum solution concentrations which can be prepared with ordinary mixing equipment vary with the molecular weight or viscosity of the polyvinyl alcohol resin. Solutions of high-viscosity polyvinyl alcohol can be readily prepared at 10 to 15 per cent solids, compared with 15 to 20 per cent for medium-viscosity resins, and 20 to 30 per cent solids for low-viscosity polyvinyl alcohol.

Film Formation

Since polyvinyl alcohol generally is dissolved in water prior to use, its film-forming abilities are of extreme importance in most applications. Polyvinyl alcohol films and coatings do not require a curing cycle, film formation occurring readily by simple evaporation of water from the solution.

When compared with plastics, the tensile strength of polyvinyl alcohol is high and when compared with other water-soluble materials, it is very impressive. The tensile strength of polyvinyl alcohol varies with a number of factors including per cent hydrolysis (see Figure 6.2), degree of polymerization, plasticizer content, and humidity.

When other factors remain constant, the tensile strength increases with the degree of polymerization. For example, films cast from unplasticized polyvinyl alcohols of high, medium, and low viscosity and conditioned at 35 per cent relative humidity showed average tensile strengths of 18,000, 17,000, and 9,000 psi, respectively.

Tensile strength values decrease as the degree of alcoholysis decreases. For example, at 50 per cent relative humidity, films cast from a completely

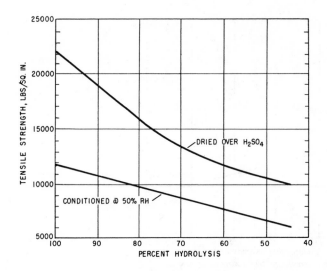

FIGURE 6.2 Relation between tensile strength and per cent hydrolysis for unplasticized polyvinyl alcohol film.

alcoholized, high-viscosity polyvinyl alcohol have tensile strengths approximately 20 per cent higher than films cast from a high-viscosity polyvinyl alcohol which is only 88 per cent alcoholized.

Addition of plasticizer, such as glycerin, to polyvinyl alcohol results in a decrease in film tensile strength (see Figure 6.3), although such addition markedly improves the elongation characteristics of the film. Elongation varies from less than 10 per cent to more than 600 per cent as a direct result of plasticizer addition, as shown in Figure 6.4.

Oil and Solvent Resistance

Polyvinyl alcohols are unaffected by animal and vegetable oils, greases, and petroleum hydrocarbons. Resistance to organic solvents increases with the degree of hydrolysis. There is no appreciable difference in the solvent resistance of low-, medium-, and high-viscosity grades within a specific hydrolysis range.

Partially hydrolyzed grades are substantially unaffected by most esters, ethers, ketones, aliphatic and aromatic hydrocarbons, and the higher monohydric alcohols. Lower monohydric alcohols have some solvent or swelling action on the partially hydrolyzed grades, but the effect of these solvents on the completely hydrolyzed grades is negligible.

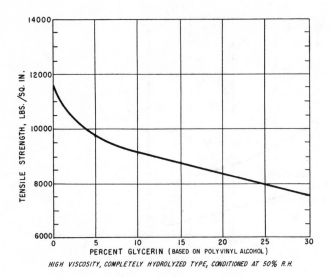

HIGH VISCOSITY, COMPLETELY HYDROLYZED TYPE, CONDITIONED AT 50% R.H.

FIGURE 6.3   Relation between tensile strength and plasticizer content of polyvinyl alcohol film.

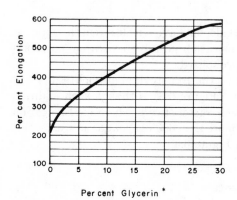

Per cent Glycerin *

FIGURE 6.4   Relation between elongation and plasticizer content of polyvinyl alcohol film (high-viscosity, completely hydrolyzed type; conditioned at 50 per cent RH).

Adhesive-Binding Properties

Another of the more important properties of polyvinyl alcohol is its adhesive or binding strength. Much of this can be attributed to its ease of film formation and the resultant high tensile strengths previously discussed. As a result, polyvinyl alcohol is one of the most valuable resins available to adhesive compounders and shares the honor with polyvinyl acetate emulsion for creating the synethetic-resin adhesives industry.

Closely allied to the adhesive properties of polyvinyl alcohol are its binding properties. In adhesive applications, polyvinyl alcohol is used to bond or laminate two surfaces; in binder applications, it serves to bond a number of particles, fibers, or other materials.

Gas Impermeability

An outstanding property of polyvinyl alcohol is its high degree of impermeability to many gases. Continuous films or coatings of polyvinyl alcohol, either plasticized or unplasticized, provide excellent barriers for such gases as oxygen, nitrogen, carbon dioxide, hydrogen, helium, and hydrogen sulfide. Permeability to oxygen, for example, is extremely low compared with that of other polymers used as packaging films. Table 6.3 shows the effect of humidity on oxygen permeability of a plasticized film of fully hydrolyzed polyvinyl alcohol.

TABLE 6.3.   Permeability of Polyvinyl Alcohol* at 3C.

Relative Humidity, %	Permeability at 1 ATM cc/100 sq in./24 hr/mil	g/100 sq in./24 hr/mil
<60	<0.04	<0.000057
60–80	<2	<0.0029
100	54 ± 3	<0.077 ± .004

* Medium viscosity, completely hydrolyzed plasticized with 16 per cent glycerine.

Notable exceptions to the low permeability of polyvinyl alcohol to gases are ammonia and water vapor. The water vapor transmission rate of an unplasticized film of medium viscosity, fully hydrolyzed polyvinyl alcohol at two different humidity gradients is shown in Table 6.4.

TABLE 6.4.   Water Vapor Transmission Rate* of Polyvinyl Alcohol Film.

Thickness (Mils)	R.H. at Film Faces, %	G. H_2O/100 sq in./ 24 hr	G. H_2O/sq in./ 24 hr
3	0/50	0.45	7.0
3	50/72	9.5	147

* ASTM E-96-53-T — Temperature 72F.

APPLICATIONS FOR POLYVINYL ALCOHOL

Industrial applications for polyvinyl alcohol that are dependent on one or more of the previously discussed properties of the resin are: adhesives, binders, paper sizing and coating, textile sizing and finishing, emulsifying, dispersing, chemical intermediate, and unsupported film.

Adhesives

The high-tensile strength and adhesive characteristics of polyvinyl alcohol have resulted in extensive use in adhesive manufacture. The types are widely diversified — from high-wet-strength adhesives for paper to remoistenable adhesives.

Polyvinyl alcohol, alone or combined with extenders, pigments, and insolubilizers, is used extensively in the preparation of high-wet-strength adhesives for paper. Combinations of polyvinyl alcohol with starch or clay are especially effective and economical. Small proportions of polyvinyl alcohol substantially increase the strength and water resistance of starch and dextrin adhesives. When maximum water resistance is required, completely alcoholized grades of polyvinyl alcohol should be used.

Adhesives such as described in U.S. Patents 2,413,570 and 2,487,448, assigned to the Du Pont Company, have outstanding water resistance. These adhesives, essentially mixtures of polyvinyl alcohol and starch extended with an acid-type clay, have the advantage of better machinability than the urea-formaldehyde resins. Applications for water-resistant adhesives based on polyvinyl alcohol include use in boxboard, wallboard, and paper bags.

The partially hydrolyzed grades of polyvinyl alcohol are usually selected for use in remoistenable adhesives since they are more sensitive to cold water than the completely hydrolyzed grades. When polyvinyl alcohol is used as a remoistenable adhesive, the curl tendencies of the coated paper are reduced, and less blocking at high humidities occurs.

Binders

Polyvinyl alcohol is a highly efficient binder for a wide variety of materials including textile fibers. It is also used as a binder for catalyst pellets, cork, plaster, and waste products. As a binder in ceramics, polyvinyl alcohol imparts high green strength and good extrusion properties, thereby reducing breakage. The effect of addition of a low-viscosity, partially hydrolyzed grade of polyvinyl alcohol to clay bodies and plaster of Paris is shown in Figure 6.5.

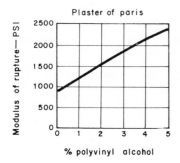

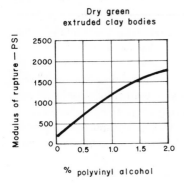

FIGURE 6.5 Effect of adding polyvinyl alcohol (low-viscosity, partially hydrolyzed type) to plaster and clay.

Polyvinyl alcohols are used as binders for nonwoven fabric and ribbon, showing excellent adhesion to both cotton and rayon fibers. In most applications where polyvinyl alcohol acts as a binder, excellent results can be obtained by using as little as 3 to 5 per cent polyvinyl alcohol solids.

Paper Sizing

Polyvinyl alcohol offers paper manufacturers a water-soluble resin which is useful in strengthening, transparentizing, greaseproofing, gasproofing, and otherwise improving the printing qualities of paper products. Conventional sizing and coating equipment can be used to apply the water solutions to paper.

For most paper-sizing applications, the completely hydrolyzed grades of polyvinyl alcohol are used in order to obtain maximum strength and water resistance. These grades have less tendency to stick to calender rolls and drying cylinders than do the partially hydrolyzed grades. Polyvinyl alcohol solutions can be conveniently applied to paper at the size press or calender stacks.

When sizing at the calender stack, the polyvinyl alcohol solution should be applied from water boxes on unheated rolls, and it may be necessary to add paraffin wax to prevent sticking to the rolls. If paraffin wax is needed, 25 to 50 per cent (based on the dry weight of the resin) of an emulsion such as Alwax* 251C size or Paracol** 600 water-dispersible wax emulsion is suggested.

The solution concentration varies with the absorbency of the paper and the viscosity of the polyvinyl alcohol. A 3 per cent solution of a high-viscosity resin is generally applied at the calender stack, although higher concentrations of lower viscosity grades can also be handled with no difficulty.

Grease-resistant papers can be produced by surface sizing with polyvinyl alcohol. If absolute grease-resistance is required, a continuous coating must be applied. Printed areas on paper sized with polyvinyl alcohol show higher gloss as a result of reduced ink penetration, as well as a smoother finish due to more even distribution of the ink. For some time this has been a popular boxboard application.

Surprisingly small amounts of polyvinyl alcohol are required to increase substantially the strength and flexibility of bond, ledger, index, blueprint, and many other high-quality papers. For example, a 2.5 per cent solution of a high-viscosity, completely hydrolyzed type of polyvinyl alcohol applied by means of a size press to 24-pound, 100 per cent rag paper stock increased the Mullen burst strength 52 per cent and the Schopper fold test value 78 per cent in the machine direction and 126 per cent in the cross direction.

Glassine paper sized with polyvinyl alcohol has improved strength, transparency, gloss, grease resistance, and dimensional stability. It is affected less by humidity and aging as polyvinyl alcohol is less hygroscopic than some transparentizing agents and does not volatilize.

If polyvinyl alcohol is properly applied to paper surfaces producing a continuous film without pinholes or breaks, the paper is absolutely grease-proof and highly impervious to oxygen and many other gases. Such papers are useful in the manufacture of containers for oils, greases, and chemicals. Since polyvinyl alcohol does not adhere well to such materials as asphalt and resins, it can be used as a coating on paper intended for packaging these materials.

* Registered trademark of American Cyanamid Company.
** Registered trademark of Hercules Inc.

Paper Coatings

Polyvinyl alcohol is well suited as a binder in pigmented coatings for paper. The ratio of binder to pigment is unusually low, and the aqueous dispersions flow on smoothly, producing tougher, whiter coatings with improved printing qualities. Good results can be obtained with as little as 2 to 4 parts of polyvinyl alcohol to 100 parts of clay.

High-viscosity or medium-viscosity grades are generally used as binders for pigmented coatings. Where economic limits are severe, combinations of starch and polyvinyl alcohol may be used satisfactorily. For initial trials, 1 part of polyvinyl alcohol to 9 parts of a low-viscosity, oxidized starch is suggested. Even in smaller proportions, polyvinyl alcohol mixed with starch produces a noticeable improvement over the starch alone. The water resistance of pigmented coatings in which polyvinyl alcohol alone or in combination with starch is used as a binder can be increased by use of insolubilizers such as dimethylolurea or trimethylolmelamine.

Pigmented coatings containing polyvinyl alcohol can be applied with the various types of coating equipment in general use.

Textile Sizing and Finishing

High tensile strength, flexibility, good abrasion resistance, and adhesion, combined with water solubility, clearly indicate the usefulness of polyvinyl alcohol as a textile size. The size can be applied by the customary slashing, skein, and single-thread methods to warp, filling, and knitting yarns.

Good results are being obtained with all types of filament and spun yarns, including the hard-to-size synthetics. Readily soluble in water, polyvinyl alcohol can be easily removed from the grey goods. In some cases it can be removed in the dyebath without a desizing operation.

One of the most important advantages of using polyvinyl alcohol as a warp size is its low biochemical oxygen demand (B.O.D.). Test results shown in Figure 6.6 indicate that polyvinyl alcohol has 5-day B.O.D. of only 200 parts per million, compared with a 5-day value of 5,000 for starch.

Polyvinyl alcohol also finds wide use as a textile finish, particularly in combination with thermosetting resins.

Emulsifying Agent

An important property of polyvinyl alcohol is its ability to function as a nonionic emulsifying agent. As such, it exhibits certain advantages over a variety of other emulsifiers. It behaves primarily as a protective colloid and tolerates substantial concentrations of electrolytes, particularly acids.

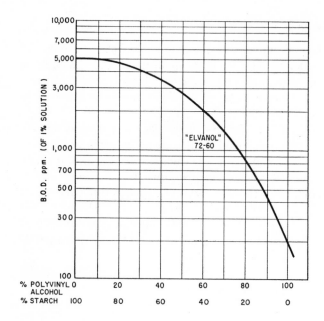

FIGURE 6.6   Five-day biochemical oxygen demand values for polyvinyl alcohol.

Moreover, it forms synergistic emulsifying combinations with certain
surface-active agents. Enhanced emulsifying action and less thickening
often result with such combinations.

Polyvinyl alcohol can be used to emulsify or disperse a large number of
materials including vegetable oils, mineral oils, solvents, plasticizers, waxes,
and resins. Although it functions both as a surface-active agent and protective colloid, and is a good emulsifying agent when used alone, results are
sometimes improved by the addition of a small amount of a product such as
Duponol* ME dry surface active agent — powder, which is particularly
effective in lowering the interfacial tension. Stable emulsions can be made
with polyvinyl alcohol in both acid and alkaline media. In some applications, it serves as a binder and thickener as well as an emulsifying agent.

In general, the partially hydrolyzed grades of polyvinyl alcohol are more
effective emulsifying agents than the completely hydrolyzed grades, with
the high-viscosity grades being more effective than the low viscosity grades.

Generally 2 to 5 per cent polyvinyl alcohol, based on the total weight of
the emulsion, should be used for oil-in-water type emulsions containing 30
to 50 per cent of the dispersed phase. For initial tests, 3 per cent polyvinyl

* Registered trademark of E. I. du Pont de Nemours & Company.

alcohol alone or 2.5 per cent polyvinyl alcohol and 0.5 per cent of a surface-active agent is suggested.

Polyvinyl Alcohol Films

Many uses in the manufacture of containers, including bags and paper-container liners for oils, greases, paints, and chemicals, have been suggested for polyvinyl alcohol films. The packaging of unit quantities of materials such as soap, dry bleaches, bluing, bath salts, insecticides, and disinfectants in water-soluble containers facilitates their use.

Preweighted quantities can be added to the water without breaking the packages or removing the wrappers, thereby saving time and reducing material losses. Sealed bags made from this film can be used for vacuum or gas packing of materials which need protection from oxygen to preserve their properties.

Polyvinyl alcohol film has been used for making oxygen tents; in vacuum or bag molding; as a wrapping for polished metal requiring protection from gases, such as oxygen and hydrogen sulfide; and as a water-soluble backing for embroidered lace during its manufacture with Schiffli equipment. When oriented by stretching, the film polarizes light. This unique property is advantageous in the manufacture of sunglasses, desk lamps, automobile headlights and windshields, and in certain photographic techniques. Because of its low degree of adhesion to several other plastic materials, polyvinyl alcohol film prevents sticking to molds.

Where maximum film strength and solvent resistance are desired, completely hydrolyzed grades of high or medium viscosity are suggested. For cold-water-soluble film, partially hydrolyzed grades are used.

Ceramics

Several ceramic applications have been found for polyvinyl alcohol. One such use is in the manufacture of fine china flatware. As little as 0.1 per cent polyvinyl alcohol, based on the dry weight of the clay, when added to a "short" casting slip improves the working characteristics.

Another ceramic use is as a temporary binder. For example, 2 to 3 per cent polyvinyl alcohol, based on the dry weight of the ceramic body, gives good results in the manufacture of steatite tubing. Solubility in water assures uniform distribution of the binder. Using polyvinyl alcohol as the binder, less pressure is required for extruding steatite; and tubing with smoother walls is produced. The extra strength derived from the binder reduces losses due to handling and machining.

Reports indicate that a small amount of polyvinyl alcohol added to steatite produces soft granules that handle easily in the automatic machines for dry molding, and gives unusually good molding characteristics. Polyvinyl alcohol has also given good results as a binder for glaze compositions. For this application, 1.0 per cent polyvinyl alcohol based on dry weight of glaze composition is recommended.

Molded Products

Plasticized polyvinyl alcohol can be molded into rubber-like articles ranging in durometer hardness from 10 to 100. High strength, flexibility, resistance to grease and organic solvents, imperviousness to gases, and good aging ability characterize these articles. They are not suitable for applications requiring a high degree of water resistance. Polyvinyl alcohol is available in the form of tubing, rod, sheeting, and a variety of molded articles.

Protective Coatings

Polyvinyl alcohol has been used as a temporary protective coating to prevent scratching of highly polished metals and plastic materials during fabrication and shipment. Having very little adhesion to these materials and being water soluble, coatings can be stripped or washed off easily with water when no longer required. Polyvinyl alcohol is also useful for protecting metals from the tarnishing effect of gases. Coatings based on polyvinyl alcohol are used to protect white sidewall tires from dirt and scuffing during shipping. The coating is removed by stripping or washing off.

Cosmetics

The emulsifying, binding, film-forming, and thickening properties of polyvinyl alcohol have all found use in cosmetic preparations. Highly stable emulsions of natural fats and oils can be prepared with partially hydrolyzed grades of polyvinyl alcohol. Cold creams, cleansing creams, shaving creams, and facial masks based on polyvinyl alcohol have been formulated.

The U.S. Food and Drug Administration has advised that they have no objection to the use of Elvanol polyvinyl alcohol in external cosmetic preparations in concentrations up to 7.5 per cent.

Stencil Screens

Polyvinyl alcohol applied from water solutions containing a dichromate such as ammonium dichromate becomes water-insoluble when exposed to ultraviolet light. This property is utilized in the preparation of stencil screens and photolithographic printing plates.

Stencil screens prepared from polyvinyl alcohol are widely used for the decoration of ceramic products. As a light-sensitive coating for stencil screens polyvinyl alcohol has several advantages including uniformity, ease of application, good dimensional stability, and long life.

Chemical Intermediate

One of the largest volume applications for polyvinyl alcohol is its use as a chemical intermediate. Polyvinyl butyral, well-known as the interlayer in safety glass, is typical of an acetal obtained by reacting polyvinyl alcohol with an aldehyde. Published literature cites many examples of other polyvinyl alcohol reaction products which offer interesting possibilities.

The reaction of polyvinyl alcohol with acrylonitrile, disclosed in U.S. Patent 2,341,553, yields an extremely gummy product which should find merit in pressure-sensitive adhesives. The use of polyvinyl alcohol as a polyol for production of fatty acid esters with quick-drying, unusual abrasive properties is described in the May, 1952, issue of *Paint & Varnish Production*. Unsaturated esters of polyvinyl alcohol are also described in the February, 1956, issue of the *Journal of Oil & Colour Chemists' Association*.

Another application utilizing polyvinyl alcohol's chemical reactivity is the production of textile fibers. In this process, polyvinyl alcohol fibers are insolubilized by reacting with formaldehyde and "orienting" after the spinning operation. Fabrics from this fiber are washable and have hand and absorbency closely resembling cotton.

Steel Quenchant

Dilute water solutions of high-viscosity, partially hydrolyzed polyvinyl alcohol give cooling rates intermediate between those obtained with oil and with water. When mixed in concentrations as dilute as 0.05 to 0.3 per cent by weight, a polyvinyl alcohol quench eliminates cracking that occurs with water and also yields a sufficient hardening response which is lacking when oil is used. Both spray and bath quenching are satisfactory.

COMPOUNDING AND MODIFYING POLYVINYL ALCOHOL

Polyvinyl alcohol solutions are generally modified prior to use to change or control characteristics of the end product. Typical modifications include addition of plasticizers, insolubilizers, extenders, defoamers, etc.

Plasticizers

Plasticizers which have been found to be most effective in imparting softness and flexibility to polyvinyl alcohol are some of the high-boiling-point, water-soluble organic compounds containing hydroxyl, amide, or amino groups. The ester-type, water-immiscible plasticizers commonly used with plastics are not compatible with polyvinyl alcohol.

At present the most widely used plasticizer for polyvinyl alcohol is glycerin. It is compatible in substantial proportions with both the partially and completely hydrolyzed types and has good stability, resistance to extraction by organic solvents, and high softening effect.

Ethylene glycol and some of the lower polyethylene glycols also act as plasticizers for polyvinyl alcohol. Triethylene glycol is particularly recommended for use with the partially hydrolyzed types in the formation of extremely soft, resilient compositions.

Tetraethylene, hexaethylene, and nonaethylene glycols are also useful plasticizers. They have lower vapor pressures than triethylene glycol but compatibility with polyvinyl alcohol decreases as the molecular weights of the glycols increase. In general, the polyethylene glycols are less compatible than glycerin with the completely hydrolyzed grades of polyvinyl alcohol.

Ethanol acetamide and ethanol formamide have been found to be effective plasticizers for polyvinyl alcohol, particularly the partially hydrolyzed grades. Formamide is compatible in substantial proportions and has a high softening effect, but the plasticizing action is only temporary because of its high vapor pressure. Ethanolamine salts, such as the acetate and the hydrochloride of triethanolamine, can be used for plasticizing both the completely and partially hydrolyzed types. Except in very dry atmospheres, sodium and ammonium thiocyanates can be used as plasticizers. Since plasticizers are hygroscopic, and since water is very effective in imparting softness and elasticity to polyvinyl alcohol, plasticity varies to some extent with humidity. The flexibility is reduced and the hardness increased at low temperatures and humidities.

Extenders

The addition of materials such as starch, dextrin, gelatin, casein, and urea to polyvinyl alcohol compositions to lower the cost is advantageous in some cases. In other cases, the advantages of a lower cost per pound is lost because the desired results cannot be obtained with the extended polyvinyl alcohol.

Compatibility with starch varies with both the grade of starch and the type of polyvinyl alcohol. In general, the compatibility increases with the per cent hydrolysis and viscosity of the polyvinyl alcohol. Several of the low-viscosity oxidized starches have been found suitable for use with polyvinyl alcohol as a size for paper. Starches have also been used in combination with polyvinyl alcohol for warp sizing.

Only small proportions of most grades of dextrin are compatible with polyvinyl alcohol. Solution compatibility is favored by low total solids. The dextrin which has been found to be most compatible with polyvinyl alcohol is a 100 per cent cold-water-soluble type of yellow potato dextrin. This dextrin usually can be mixed in all proportions, provided the total solids are less than 15 per cent.

Stable mixtures of solutions of some photographic and pharmaceutical grades of gelatins and polyvinyl alcohol can be made, but most low-quality gelatins and glues are not compatible.

When used as an extender, casein should be dissolved in an alkaline material, such as ammonium hydroxide, which does not precipitate the polyvinyl alcohol. The polyvinyl alcohol solution should also be made alkaline before adding to the casein solution. Borax and sodium carbonate should not be used to dissolve the casein since only very small amounts of these salts are required to gel or precipitate polyvinyl alcohol.

In addition to serving as an extender, urea has a slight plasticizing effect on polyvinyl alcohol. Water-soluble urea-formaldehyde and phenol-formaldehyde resins can be used both to lower the price and increase the water resistance of polyvinyl alcohol compositions. It is customary to use 10 to 30 per cent of these resins, based on the weight of the polyvinyl alcohol. Low-priced pigments such as clay and whiting also make useful extenders.

It is often advisable to use a surface-active agent to facilitate dispersion of the extender pigments and also to decrease the viscosity. Tetrasodium pyrophosphate, at a concentration of about 0.3 per cent based on the weight of pigment, is suggested for this purpose.

Low-cost waste sulfite liquor products can be used as extenders. However, these materials increase the viscosity and, since they are highly colored, impart considerable color to solutions.

Insolubilizers

Several practical methods for increasing the water resistance of polyvinyl alcohol exist. However, since even after such treatments the products tend to soften, swell, and lose strength on exposure to water, polyvinyl alcohol is not recommended where moistureproofness or a high degree of water resistance is required.

For maximum water resistance, completely hydrolyzed grades of polyvinyl alcohol are chosen. Methods of increasing the water resistance of polyvinyl alcohol include heat treatment and the addition of inorganic acids, dibasic organic acids, various metal salts, titanium organics, and aldehydes or water-soluble formaldehyde derivatives. Insolubilized films of polyvinyl alcohol can be dissolved in a hot 3 per cent solution of hydrogen peroxide.

Precipitants and Gelling Agents

A number of organic and inorganic compounds precipitate polyvinyl alcohol from water solutions or cause gelling. Such agents are sometimes useful in applications where it is advantageous to control the penetration of polyvinyl alcohol solutions into porous surfaces.

Only small amounts of some salts are required to precipitate polyvinyl alcohol from water solutions, whereas others are tolerated in large proportions. Salts illustrating the latter class are potassium iodide, sodium nitrate, zinc chloride, potassium thiocyanate, and calcium chloride. Salts typical of the former class are sodium carbonate, potassium sulfate, and sodium sulfate. These salts will cause polyvinyl alcohol to precipitate from solution if the salt content of the solution exceeds 4 per cent.

One of the most effective gelling agents for polyvinyl alcohol is borax. As little as 0.1 per cent borax, based on weight of solution, causes a 5 per cent solution of completely hydrolyzed polyvinyl alcohol to gel. Partially hydrolyzed grades of polyvinyl alcohol tolerate greater quantities of borax.

Ammonium hydroxide and a number of acids including hydrochloric, sulfuric, nitric, acetic, and phosphoric are tolerated in large proportions by polyvinyl alcohol solutions. Considerably smaller percentages of sodium hydroxide and boric acid precipitate polyvinyl alcohol solutions.

A number of dyes and other organic compounds, when added to solutions of completely hydrolyzed grades of polyvinyl alcohol, form thermally reversible gels. Solutions containing gelling agents, which are gels at room temperature and fluids when hot, are useful in certain dipping and coating operations to prevent draining. Congo red is one of the most effective gelling agents for polyvinyl alcohol; 3 per cent Congo red, based on dry weight of the polyvinyl alcohol, added to a 10 per cent solution of completely hydrolyzed polyvinyl alcohol produces a composition which is fluid and easily applied at temperatures above 50C (122F) and is a firm gel at room temperature. Most gelling agents are not effective with partially hydrolyzed grades of polyvinyl alcohol.

Pigments and Dyes

Care should be exercised in the selection of pigments and dyes as some cause gelling or thickening of polyvinyl alcohol solutions. This may result from the presence of large proportions of soluble salts or from the action of the coloring agents themselves. Only a small percentage of soluble salts should be permitted in pigments and dyes to be used with polyvinyl alcohol.

Wetting Agents

Practically any of the common wetting agents can be used with polyvinyl alcohol solutions. The amount required varies with the conditions but is usually 0.05 to 0.20 per cent, based on the weight of the solution.

Antifoaming Agents

Foaming of polyvinyl alcohol solutions can be reduced by raising the temperature, reducing the amount of agitation, or adding a defoamer. Lorol 20* fatty alcohol technical, Bubble Breaker 259**, and AntifoamA*** silicone compound are among the defoamers which have proved to be suitable for use with polyvinyl alcohol. If a defoamer is necessary, about 0.1 per cent, based on the weight of the solution, should be added during the preparation of the solution. If foam develops later, additional defoamer can be added as required. Lanolubric #2****, at concentrations of 1 to 2 per cent, based on dry weight of polyvinyl alcohol, has been found to be a permanent antifoam.

COMMERCIAL ASPECTS

The price of polyvinyl alcohol has decreased markedly in the past few years which has helped extend its use into many new applications. The bulk price of fully hydrolyzed polyvinyl alcohol has been reduced from 57 cents per pound F.O.B. plant to 45 cents per pound delivered, a reduction of more than 20 per cent. A review of prices of the natural products that compete with polyvinyl alcohol show the price differential has narrowed even further. For example, during the time when the price of PVA was decreasing, the price of casein was fluctuating from 18 cents per pound to 30 cents per pound. While prices of several other basic natural products have not increased, many of them are being modified to increase their utility, and the modified products are priced higher than the basic material.

In many instances, manufacturers now find that, although polyvinyl alcohol may be more expensive than other raw materials on a cents per pound basis, overall economics favor PVA. For example, one pound of polyvinyl alcohol is capable of replacing about three pounds of casein in paper-coating formulations. On a straight cost comparison, this replacement ratio

* Registered trademark of E. I. du Pont de Nemours & Company.
** Registered trademark of Balab, Inc., Oakland, Calif.
*** Registered trademark of Dow Corning Corporation.
**** Registered trademark of E. F. Houghton Company.

readily justifies replacement of casein as a pigment binder. The use of PVA for paper coatings has continued to increase, not only for these economic considerations, but also because polyvinyl alcohol can be tailored to satisfy specific end-use requirements.

Polyvinyl alcohol is currently experiencing extensive growth in the textile warp sizing field. The unique performance properties referred to earlier have permitted polyvinyl alcohol to replace other sizing materials in many applications.

Polyvinyl alcohol films have achieved new importance as the demand for gas-barrier properties grows. The bulk of the film use now is in low-pressure vacuum bag molding where the property of low adhesion to most plastic and metal materials allows the film to be stripped readily from the article. PVA films may also find utility in film laminate structures designed for long-term food packaging where advantage can be taken of PVA's impermeability to oxygen, fats, and oils.

The use of PVA in adhesives and emulsifier systems has continued to expand as the use of synthetic adhesive systems has increased. The need for more demanding adhesive properties as in paperboard laminates has stimulated the use of PVA based adhesives. Polyvinyl alcohol provides increased production efficiency, greater bonding versatility, and more water resistance.

In summary, polyvinyl alcohol offers industry a polymer with a wide range of controllable water solubility, an excellent ability to form films with outstanding tensile strength, grease and solvent resistance, and gas impermeability. The polymer is also an effective disperser, emulsion stabilizer, adhesive, and binder.

This balance of properties, found only in polyvinyl alcohol, makes it one of industry's most unusual and versatile polymers.

Julian L. Azorlosa
Anthony J. Martinelli[1]

7

Central Research Laboratory
General Aniline and Film Corporation
Easton, Pennsylvania

Polyvinylpyrrolidone

Polyvinylpyrrolidone is a relative newcomer among the commercial water-soluble polymers produced within the United States. In early 1956, the General Aniline and Film Corporation began full-scale production after several years of commercial development. Polyvinylpyrrolidone is usually referred to by the shorthand designation of PVP. Special pharmaceutical grades are sold by General Aniline under the Plasdone* trademark. Beverage grades have been offered recently under the Polyclar* label. For specific uses in the textile industry, a formulated aqueous solution is sold as Peregal ST.* German-produced PVP has been marketed in Europe under various trade names: Albigen A,** Kollidon,** Luviskol,** and Igecoll.**

Chemically, PVP is a homopolymer of N-vinylpyrrolidone:

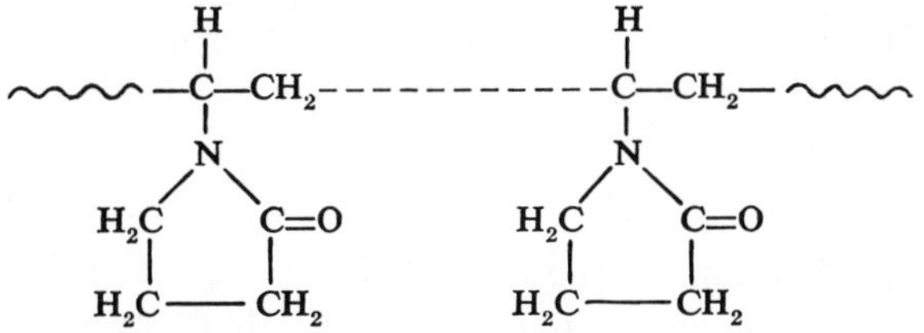

MANUFACTURE OF PVP

The synthesis of PVP was developed in Germany by Dr. J. W. Reppe and his associates of the Badische Anilin und Soda Fabrik during the late nineteen thirties. It was an outgrowth of a technological breakthrough in the safe handling of high-pressure acetylene. This six-step synthesis, shown in

[1] Deceased.
* Registered trademarks of General Aniline and Film Corporation.
** Trademarks of Badische Anilin und Soda Fabrik.

Figure 7.1, is used by General Aniline at its Calvert, Kentucky plant. The basic raw materials employed are acetylene, formaldehyde, ammonia, and hydrogen.

The four viscosity grades currently offered for industrial use are listed in Table 7.1. PVP K-15, PVP K-30, and PVP K-90 are in powder form. Aqueous solutions of the PVP K-60 and K-90 grades are available also.

TABLE 7.1.   Industrial Grades of PVP.

Grade*	K-15	K-30	K-60	K-90
Form	white, free-flowing powder	white, free-flowing powder	aqueous solution	aqueous solution (or granular)
Active ingredient content, min, %	95	95	45	20 (95)
Bulk Density, lb/cu ft	25–26	25–26	—	—
Moisture, max, %	5	5	55	80 (5)
Ash, max,** %	0.02	0.02	0.02	0.02
Unsaturation as monomer, max,** %	1.0	1.0	1.0	1.0
Approximate molecular weight, viscometric	10,000	40,000	160,000	360,000

* The K-values assigned to various grades of PVP represent a function of the mean molecular weight:

$$\frac{\log \eta \text{ rel}}{c} = \frac{75K_o^2}{1 + 1.5K_o c} + K_o$$

$$K = 1000K_o$$

Where c = concentration in gm/100 ml solution.
η rel = viscosity of the solution compared to solvent.

** Based on PVP content.

Since General Aniline is the only PVP producer in the United States, production figures are not available. The price structure as of August, 1967, is shown in the following tabulation for both the industrial and pharmaceutical grades:

Non-Pharmaceutical	Bulk Price, $ per lb (1967)
PVP K-15, powder	1.50
PVP K-30, powder	1.25
PVP K-60, 45% in water	1.25*
PVP K-90, 20% in water	1.50*
PVP K-90, powder	1.75
Pharmaceutical	
Plasdone Types	2.67
Plasdone C (plasma grade)	3.25

* Based on solids.

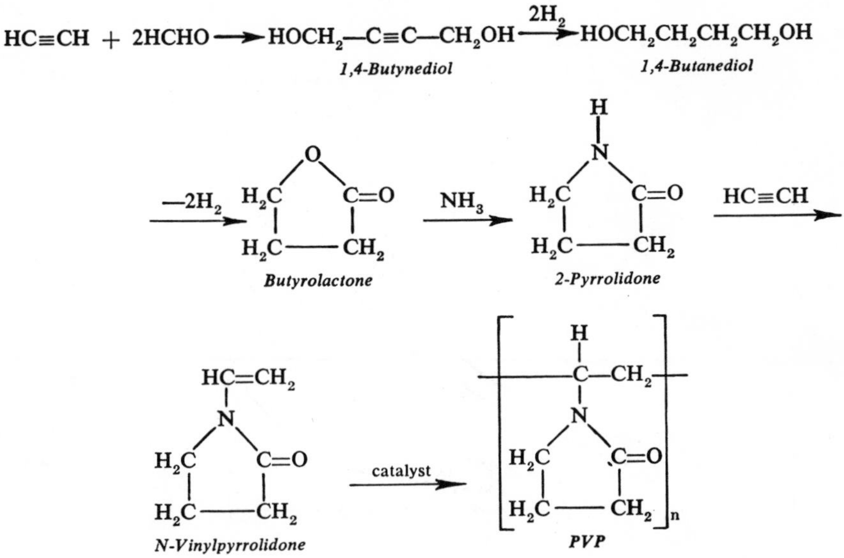

$$HC\equiv CH + 2HCHO \longrightarrow HOCH_2\text{---}C\equiv C\text{---}CH_2OH \xrightarrow{2H_2} HOCH_2CH_2CH_2CH_2OH$$

1,4-Butynediol   1,4-Butanediol

Butyrolactone   2-Pyrrolidone

N-Vinylpyrrolidone   PVP

FIGURE 7.1 Synthesis of PVP.

PROPERTIES OF PVP

The commercial versatility of PVP is inherent in the following properties: wide solubility and compatibility range, complexing and detoxifying ability, physiological acceptability, protective-colloid action, film-forming ability, and adhesive qualities.

Film Properties

PVP may be cast from a variety of solvents to give films which are clear, glossy, and hard at low humidities. They exhibit excellent adhesion to a wide variety of surfaces including glass, metals, and plastics. Unmodified films of PVP are hygroscopic. The degree of water absorption as a function of relative humidity is shown in Figure 7.2. CMC (carboxymethylcellulose) and polyvinyl alcohol are included for comparison.

The dry film has a density (d_4^{25}) of 1.25 and a refractive index (n_D^{25}) of 1.53. Tackiness at higher humidities may be minimized by incorporating compatible, water-insensitive modifiers such as 10 per cent of an aryl-sulfonamide-formaldehyde resin.

Aqueous Solutions

PVP powder may be readily dissolved by portion-wise addition to rapidly stirred water. Heat will accelerate the process. The effect of concentration

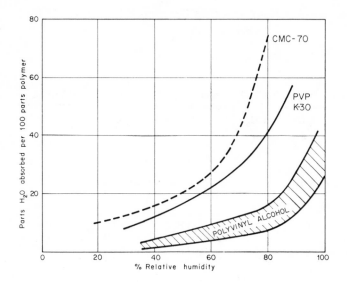

FIGURE 7.2   Comparative hygroscopicity of PVP.

on aqueous solution viscosity for the various commercial grades is illustrated in Figure 7.3.

Viscosity is essentially independent of pH over the range of 0 to 10. In concentrated HCl the viscosity increases; in strong caustic the PVP precipitates out.

Aqueous solutions of PVP exhibit a high tolerance for many inorganic salts (Table 7.2). Lowering the molecular weight increases the salt tolerance.

Aqueous PVP is stable on prolonged storage if protected from mold growth. For this purpose such additives as sorbic acid and the chlorophenols have been found effective at 0.1 to 0.2 per cent based on the PVP.

Solubility

In comparison with other commercially available water-soluble polymers, the wide solubility of PVP in organic solvents is unusual. However, in this connection one must differentiate between the commercial PVP powders containing up to 5 per cent moisture and the anhydrous form. As Table 7.3 indicates, the anhydrous material has an even wider range of solvents.

Compatibility

PVP is compatible with a variety of resins and modifiers including both the hydrophilic and hydrophobic types. Table 7.4 includes representative

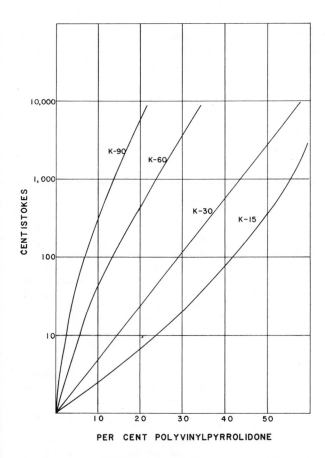

CENTISTOKES

PER CENT POLYVINYLPYRROLIDONE

FIGURE 7.3 Viscosity of aqueous PVP solutions.

examples. Table 7.5 illustrates the effect of hydrophilic and hydrophobic modifiers on PVP films.

Effect of Heat

When PVP films are heated at 130C in air for several hours, some yellowing will occur without insolubilization. Prolonged heating in air at 150C will cause cross-linking. However, in an inert atmosphere PVP can tolerate temperatures of 250C for several minutes without significant degradation.

Aqueous PVP can be gelled and permanently insolubilized by heating with alkali. For example, a 30 per cent water solution of PVP K-30 adjusted to a pH of 12 will gel within 4 hours at 100C.

TABLE 7.2.   Effect of Inorganic Salts on Aqueous PVP at 25C.

| Salt | | PVP K-30 | | PVP K-60 | |
		Salt Added %*	Solution Appearance	Salt Added %*	Solution Appearance
Aluminum sulfate	$Al_2(SO_4)_3 \cdot 18H_2O$	1000	Unchanged	660	Colloidal suspension
Ammonium chloride	NH_4Cl	1000	Unchanged	1000	Unchanged
Ammonium sulfate	$(NH_4)_2SO_4$	1000	Unchanged	1000	Unchanged
Barium chloride	$BaCl_2 \cdot H_2O$	1000	Unchanged	1000	Unchanged
Calcium chloride	$CaCl_2$	1000	Unchanged	1000	Unchanged
Chromium sulfate	$Cr_2(SO_4) \cdot H_2O$	1000	Unchanged	1000	Unchanged
Copper sulfate	$CuSO_4 \cdot 5H_2O$	1000	Unchanged	1000	Unchanged
Ferric chloride	$FeCl_3 \cdot 6H_2O$	1000	Unchanged	1000	Unchanged
Magnesium chloride	$MgCl_2 \cdot 6H_2O$	1000	Unchanged	1000	Unchanged
Mercuric acetate	$Hg(C_2H_3O_2)_2$	1000	Unchanged	1000	Unchanged
Nickel nitrate	$Ni(NO_3)_2 \cdot 6H_2O$	1000	Unchanged	1000	Unchanged
Lead acetate	$Pb(C_2H_3O_2)_2 \cdot 3H_2O$	1000	Unchanged	1000	Unchanged
Potassium chloride	KCl	1000	Unchanged	1000	Unchanged
Potassium sulfate	K_2SO_4	1000	Unchanged	1000	Unchanged
Potassium dichromate	$K_2Cr_2O_7$	1000	Unchanged	1000	Unchanged
Sodium carbonate	Na_2CO_3	185	Colloidal suspension	170	Colloidal suspension
Sodium chloride	$NaCl$	1000	Unchanged	1000	Unchanged
Sodium nitrate	$NaNO_3$	1000	Unchanged	1000	Unchanged
Sodium phosphate (primary)	$NaH_2PO_4 \cdot H_2O$	1000	Unchanged	1000	Unchanged
Sodium phosphate (dibasic)	$Na_2HPO_4 \cdot 7H_2O$	370	Colloidal suspension	210	Colloidal suspension
Sodium phosphate (tribasic)	$Na_3PO_4 \cdot 12H_2O$	128	Colloidal suspension	90	Colloidal suspension
Sodium pyrophosphate	$Na_4P_2O_7$	1000	Unchanged	1000	Unchanged
Sodium metasilicate	$Na_2SiO_3 \cdot 5H_2O$	300	Colloidal suspension	170	Colloidal suspension
Sodium sulfate	Na_2SO_4	1000	Unchanged	470	Colloidal suspension
Sodium sulfite	$Na_2SO_3 \cdot 7H_2O$	1000	Unchanged	1000	Unchanged
Silver nitrate	$AgNO_3$	1000	Unchanged	1000	Unchanged
Zinc sulfate	$ZnSO_4 \cdot 7H_2O$	1000	Unchanged	1000	Unchanged

* Per cent by volume of 10 per cent salt solution added to 10 per cent PVP solution. For example, when a 100 ml quantity of a 10 per cent salt solution is added to 10 ml of a 10 per cent PVP solution, the amount is expressed as 1000 per cent.

TABLE 7.3.   Solubility of PVP in Organic Solvents.

Solvents for Both Commercial PVP (up to 5 per cent H_2O) and Anhydrous PVP
  Acids: formic, acetic, propionic
  Alcohols: methanol, ethanol, butanol, 2-ethylhexanol, phenol
  Amides: dimethylformamide, N-methylpyrrolidone, 2-pyrrolidone
  Amines: aniline, morpholine, pyridine, ethanolamine, butylamine
  Polyhydroxy Compounds: ethylene glycol, glycerine, polyethylene glycols
  Halogen Compounds: methylene dichloride, chloroform
  Nitroparaffins: nitromethane, nitroethane
                 Solvents for Anhydrous PVP Only
  Cyclic Ethers: tetrahydrofuran, dioxane
  Esters: ethyl acetate, butyl acetate
  Ketones: acetone, methyl ethyl ketone, cyclohexanone
  Halogen Compounds: trichlorofluoromethane, dichlorodifluoromethane
              Non-Solvent for PVP (Anhydrous or Commercial)
  Aliphatic Hydrocarbons: hexane, cyclohexane, mineral oil, turpentine
  Ethers: diethyl ether

TABLE 7.4.   Compatibility of PVP in Films.

	Water Soluble	Water Insoluble
Compatible Resins	Corn dextrin	Cellulose acetate
	Carbowax* 1500	Cellulose triacetate
	CMC-70	Ethyl cellulose
	Gum arabic	Polyacrylonitrile
	Methyl cellulose	Polyvinyl chloride
	Polyvinyl alcohol	Polyvinyl butyral
	Sodium alginate	Polyvinyl formal
		Shellac (refined)
Plasticizers	Diethylene glycol	Dimethyl phthalate
and Modifiers	Glycerin	N-Ethyltoluenesulfonamide
	Sorbitol	Oleyl alcohol
		Nonylphenol

* Registered trademark of Union Carbide Corporation.

Complexing and Detoxifying Ability

The term "complexing" is used here to describe PVP's ability to form molecular adducts with other substances. In some cases the result is a solubilizing action; in others the result is a precipitating action. Insoluble complexes are formed when aqueous solutions of PVP are added to aqueous solutions of tannic acid, polyacrylic acid, and methyl vinyl ether-maleic

TABLE 7.5. Effect of Modifiers on PVP Films.

Modifier Used	Per Cent Modifier	Per Cent Water Absorbed at 50% Relative Humidity	Tackiness of Film	
			50% Relative Humidity	70% Relative Humidity
None	0	18	Tack-free	Slightly tacky
Glycerol	25	17	Very tacky	Very tacky
Diethylene glycol	25	17	Very tacky	Very tacky
Sorbitol	25	15	Slightly tacky	Very tacky
Santicizer E-15*	10	11	Tack-free	Slightly tacky
Dimethyl phthalate	25	9	Tack-free	Tack-free
Carboxymethylcellulose	50	13	Tack-free	Tack-free
Cellulose acetate	25	—	Tack-free	Tack-free

* Registered trademark of Monsanto Company.

anhydride copolymer (PVM/MA). These precipitates redissolve on the addition of dilute caustic. In the latter case the complex contains approximately equal weights of the two components.

PVP solubilizes and detoxifies many dyestuffs, physiological materials, and toxic chemicals. The case of iodine is illustrative. Iodine alone is soluble to the extent of 0.034 per cent in water at 25C whereas it is soluble to the extent of 0.58 per cent in a 1 per cent aqueous PVP solution, a 17-fold increase. The PVP-iodine complex retains the germicidal properties of iodine while the oral toxicity toward mammals is drastically reduced as illustrated in Table 7.6.

TABLE 7.6. Comparative Oral Toxicity* PVP-Iodine 10 Versus Lugol's Solution.

	PVP-Iodine 10 mg available Iodine per Kg of Body Wt	Lugol's Solution mg available Iodine per Kg of Body Wt
LD_0	1000	100
LD_{50}	1400	400
LD_{100}	1700	700

* White rats were dosed with aqueous solutions containing 2.5 per cent available iodine in both cases.

PVP complexes with phenolic compounds. Recent studies by the Industrial Biology Research and Testing Laboratory have shown that the full germicidal properties of the phenol are retained while the skin-irritating and sensitizing effects are minimized. Table 7.7 illustrates this effect.

TABLE 7.7. Effect of PVP in Reducing Skin Irritation of Phenolic Sanitizer-Cleaner.

| Per cent PVP in Formula | Number of Human Subjects Showing Skin Irritation | | | | | |
| | Primary Application | | | Challenge Application | | |
	No Reaction	1+ Reaction	2+ Reaction	No Reaction	1+ Reaction	2+ Reaction
0	43	6	1	39	9	2
0.05	47	3	0	43	6	1
0.25	50	0	0	46	3	1
5.0	50	0	0	50	0	0

Basic Formulation:
5% o-Benzyl-p-chlorophenol
30% Sodium dodecylbenzene sulfonate (12% active)
15% Isopropyl alcohol
0.72% Sodium hydroxide
Balance Water

Physiological Acceptability

A long clinical history has shown PVP to be an essentially physiologically inert material.

Acute oral toxicity $LD_0 = 100$ gm/kilo of body weight. Higher dosages were not used on the test animals because of the danger of mechanical injury to the digestive system.

Acute intravenous toxicity $LD_{50} = 12$ to 15 gm/kilo of body weight.

Topical application PVP was tested on humans and found to be neither a primary skin irritant nor sensitizer.

Eye irritation On repeated instillation into rabbit eyes, no signs of irritation were observed which were attributable to PVP.

Chronic oral toxicity Rats and dogs were fed 1 to 10 per cent PVP K-30 by weight of their total diet for up to 24 months. No toxic effects or significant pathology attributable to the PVP was observed.

APPLICATIONS

Pharmaceuticals

The use of PVP as a blood plasma substitute or blood volume expander was developed in Germany by the Bayer Company. The formulated product, Periston, was used extensively by the German Army and is credited with saving thousands of lives. This development was made possible because of PVP's compatibility with body fluids and its stability in storage. It has not been found to be antigenic and it eliminates the danger of infectious hepatitis associated with human plasma. However, since it is not metabolized by the body, unlimited use intravenously is not recommended. It is used extensively in Europe and is stockpiled for emergency use in the United States.

Plasdone C, a special plasma-grade PVP of a specific molecular weight range and purity, is marketed by General Aniline. The following procedure has been used in preparing PVP solutions for clinical use:

> Plasdone C powder is added to a normal saline solution (prepared from pyrogen-free water) so that the PVP concentration is 3.5 per cent on the anhydrous basis. When solution is complete, the pH is adjusted to between 5 and 7 with sodium bicarbonate. After filtration the solution is bottled, sealed, and autoclaved for approximately 30 minutes at 121C.

The complexing ability and protective colloid action of PVP have led to its extensive use as a retardant vehicle and suspending agent for drugs. As a retardant vehicle, PVP prolongs the therapeutic action of the drug and, in some cases, increases the potency. For example, PVP increases the time during which penicillin is retained in the blood stream, thereby reducing the number of injections necessary.

Investigation has shown that PVP complexes with such pharmaceuticals as chloromycetin, benzoic acid, mandelic acid, para-aminobenzoic acid, phenobarbitol, salicylic acid, sulfathiazole, and sodium para-aminosalicylate. The prolonging action has also been noted with insulin, ACTH, and various hormones. However, this effect of PVP is not general for all drugs and must be studied in each specific case.

The detoxifying action of PVP *in vivo* against certain toxins has been demonstrated in numerous clinical studies. In some cases it causes their elimination through the kidneys. The complexing ability of PVP has been utilized in developing a safe form of iodine (see Complexing and Detoxifying Ability, p. 137).

PVP-iodine 10, a complex produced by General Aniline in powder form, contains 10 per cent available iodine and is stable in storage since the resultant vapor pressure of iodine is almost zero. Commercial products such as mouthwash, antiseptic, ointment, etc., contain this broad-spectrum biocide.

It is significant that at the levels of recommended usage the toxicity of the available iodine has been drastically reduced, eliminating the necessity of a "poison" label.

The adhesiveness and lack of toxicity of PVP have led to its use in pharmaceutical tablets as a granulating agent or coating; Plasdone grade PVP K-30 is sold by General Aniline for this purpose. The classical binders such as starch or gelatin are used in water systems. However, where the ingredients are unstable in water, alcohol-soluble PVP permits granulation. The following patent example by C. J. Endicott *et al.* (U.S. Patent 2,820,741) illustrates this use of PVP:

	Pounds
Aluminum aspirin	14.64
Acetophenetidin	7.64
Caffeine alcohol	1.53
Methapyrilene HCl	1.72
Talc	0.25
Alcohol 3A	6.50
Polyvinylpyrrolidone	0.32

The ingredients are milled if necessary and then the caffeine, methapyrilene, and talc are mixed and charged into a mass mixer along with the aluminum aspirin and acetophenetidin. The dry mixture is wet with the solution of polyvinylpyrrolidone in alcohol and the material, after thorough mixing, is granulated through ¼-inch mesh screen. It is then dried at 120C and ground to a suitably small size for filling into capsules.

Cosmetics and Toiletries

PVP is now well-established as an ingredient of many cosmetic formulations. Its acceptance by the cosmetic chemist can be attributed to the following properties: adhesion to hair and skin, ability to form lustrous films, solubility in organic solvents as well as water, nonallergenic character, and protective colloid action.

U.S. Patent 2,871,161 describes the use of PVP in Freon* hair sprays. Complete solubility in the alcohol-propellant combination has eliminated the valve-clogging problem associated with the older shellac-based products. When properly compounded, the PVP film does not dust or flake on the hair. Its hygroscopicity enables the hair to be reset by the use of a wet comb, and its water solubility allows easy removal by shampooing.

* Trademark of E. I. du Pont de Nemours & Company.

While individual hair-spray formulas are secret, the basic formulation is fairly simple and can be adjusted for different climatic conditions. In a dry climate a humectant is often used, while in a moist climate a water-repellent plasticizer is employed. Aerosol hair sprays in the United States contain 1.25 to 2.0 per cent PVP. In Europe amounts up to 6 per cent have been reported. In actual use, the type of hair determines the amount to be applied, fine silky hair requiring less PVP than coarse, wiry hair. A typical formulation is as follows:

	Weight Per Cent
PVP K-30	1.5
Lanolin (alcohol soluble)	0.2
Perfume	0.2
Anhydrous ethanol (SDA-40)	28.1
Propellant mixture:	
Freon* or Genetron** 11	45.0
Freon or Genetron 12	25.0

* Trademark of E. I. du Pont de Nemours & Company.
** Trademark of General Chemical Company.

While the aerosol hair-spray market has been predominantly feminine to date, considerable effort is being directed toward evolving a masculine product. PVP is already being used in hair dressings for men. Many of the oil-in-water emulsion types contain PVP in the aqueous phase. It exerts a stabilizing influence, imparts sheen to the hair, and gives the desirable rewet-reset character.

PVP is used in shampoos to improve foam stability and impart lustre to the hair. Even after a shampoo is rinsed away, enough PVP is adsorbed on the hair to give it sheen and manageability. Its use in antiseptic shampoos holds promise in view of its effectiveness in reducing the irritation of the chlorophenol type of bacteriostats (see Complexing and Detoxifying Ability, p. 137).

The dye-complexing ability of PVP has led to its use in hair tints or color rinses. By adjusting the ratio of the PVP to dye, the tint can be made either more permanent or more transient, higher PVP concentrations favoring the latter.

PVP, which appears to impart emolliency and to reduce skin irritation, is being incorporated into preshave and after-shave lotions; 0.5 to 0.75 per cent are typical amounts used. These properties, as well as PVP's soil-suspending ability, can be utilized in hand-cream preparations and in so-called waterless hand cleaners for removing dyes and oily grime. The preceding formulation is illustrative.

In the related field of dentifrices, an interesting use of PVP has been patented by the Colgate-Palmolive Company. It was found that the PVP complexing ability could be utilized to increase the stain-removing power

	Parts by Weight
Igepal* CO-630	4.0
PVP K-30 (5% aqueous solution)	42.5
Mineral oil	35.0
Oleic acid	10.0
Monoethanolamine	1.0
Triethanolamine	3.0
Propylene glycol	4.5

The mineral oil and oleic acid are mixed with rapid stirring at room-temperature. In a separate container, the aqueous PVP K-30, the amines, Igepal CO-630 and propylene glycol are mixed. The water phase is then slowly added to the oil phase with vigorous stirring.

* Registered trademark of General Aniline and Film Corporation.

of a dental cream. The following table abstracted from Colgate's South African Patent No. 14793 demonstrates the effect of PVP on the removal of tobacco juice.

Porcelain Strip	Per cent Whiteness	Color
Unstained	100.0	Grayish white
Stained	81.2	Brown to black
Brushed with control dental cream	88.6	Brown
Brushed with cream containing		
0.125% PVP	101.0	Grayish white to white
0.25% PVP	104.0	Grayish white to white
0.5% PVP	105.3	Grayish white to white

Other products in which PVP is being investigated include barrier creams, suntan lotions, and deodorants.

Textiles

The applications of PVP in the textile industry can be related to its complexing ability and protective colloid action. PVP is a highly effective stripping assistant for removing color from cellulosic fibers, particularly the vat, sulfur, and direct dyestuffs. This action is associated with the weakly cationic nature of PVP and its ability to form cation-anion complexes with the phenolate and sulfonate groups. It is currently marketed as a formulated aqueous solution under such tradenames as Peregal ST* and Albigen A.** These products are stable to hard water and to the pH conditions normally encountered in textile processing. The following excerpt from General Aniline's Peregal ST bulletin illustrates its use in stripping vat and sulfur colors.

"A blank vat bath should be prepared to which the Peregal is added as the last component according to the following general practical formula:

$2\frac{1}{2}$–5 lb Caustic soda flakes
4 –6 lb Sodium hydrosulfite
$1\frac{1}{2}$–3 lb Peregal ST
Per 100 gallons water

Peregal ST is insolubilized by contact with concentrated caustic soda and therefore its addition to the stripping bath should be made only after dilution of the blank vat.

In general, the goods to be stripped are entered in the bath at 170 to 185F, and maintained at this or, if necessary, at higher temperatures for 30 to 45 minutes; rinsed in a bath containing one-fourth to one-half oz/gal hydrosulfite and then rinsed and finished in the usual manner."

Formulas employing Peregal ST*, zinc formaldehyde sulfoxylate, and formic acid are recommended for stripping direct and developed colors. There are indications that PVP might also be used as a dye-retarding agent in pastel dyeings.

An interesting application of this complexing action is the development of fugitive tints using PVP. In the textile industry common practice is to employ such tints on textile materials to aid in identification during processing. These tints must, of course, be removed completely and easily during the scouring operation. British Celanese's U.S. Patent No. 2,802,713 describes the preparation of a concentrated tinting solution by the addition of 1 part Chlorazol Fast Pink BK 200 per cent to 8 parts of a 30 per cent aqueous solution of PVP. In general, good results are obtained with a 6 to 1 ratio of PVP to dye on the dry basis.

The property of dye-complexing can be utilized "in reverse" by incorporating the PVP into a synthetic fiber with which the PVP is compatible. Incorporation of 5 to 10 per cent in a hydrophobic fiber increases water

* Registered trademark of General Aniline and Film Corporation.
** Registered trademark of Badische Anilin und Soda Fabrik.

affinity as well as dye receptivity. To improve the dyeability of an acrylic fiber the PVP may be added to the spinning solution. Similar effects have been noted with cellulose triacetate in the General Aniline laboratories. Thin films having the composition 90 per cent cellulose triacetate- 10 per cent PVP were cast from methylene dichloride. Boiling in water for 30 minutes and in a desizing solution (8 ounces of Igepon T* per 100 gallons of water) for 20 minutes failed to extract detectable amounts of PVP. The effect on dye receptivity is shown in Table 7.8.

TABLE 7.8. Effect of PVP on Dye Receptivity of Cellulose Triacetate Films.

	Increase in Color Intensity Over Control	
Dyed with	10% PVP K-30	10% PVP K-90
Celliton* Fast Yellow GGLL	100%	109%
Celliton* Fast Pink RF	82%	51%
Celliton* Fast Blue FFRS	47%	72%

* Registered trademark of General Aniline and Film Corporation.

The suspending action of PVP is utilized in nylon scours for removing the graphite lubricant; 0.5 per cent has been reported to be effective. In the delustering of Nylon 6 with titanium dioxide, the addition of 0.25 per cent PVP K-30 has been found effective in preventing pigment flocculation.

The use of PVP in processing sizes and finishing agents for glass fiber and fabric is being investigated. The unusual adhesion of PVP to glass can be exploited here by formulating with suitable plasticizer and lubricant.

Beverages

A significant advance in brewing technology has been the introduction of PVP as a fining and stabilizing agent for beer. This has been the result of intensive investigation by W. D. McFarlane of Canadian Breweries Ltd. One of the problems long recognized by the brewing industry has been chill haze, i.e. the cloudy appearance which often develops in refrigerated beer. A special brewer's grade of PVP K-90, offered since 1958 under the trade name Polyclar H, appears to precipitate selectively those tannins which cause chill haze. The advantages of PVP in brewing are: improved taste and taste stability; improved foam retention; better chill-haze stability; easier filtra-

* Registered trademark of General Aniline and Film Corporation.

tions; cleaner worts from the cooler; cleaner, better tasting storage beers; shorter storage time; savings on hops; and reduced enzymatic chillproof requirements.

The optimum amount of PVP used generally falls within the range of 120 to 200 parts per million or 3 to 5 pounds of PVP solids per 100 barrels of beer and must be determined experimentally for a given brewery. In brewery practice, malt, cereals, and hops are boiled with water for a specified period. The hot liquid, strained free of hops, is called the "hot wort." Usually the best results are obtained by adding the PVP a few minutes before the end of the kettle boil or in the hot wort receiver. Table 7.9 summarizes the results of a series of brewery runs.

As can be observed, the PVP content of the finished beer is practically nil. Further addition of up to 100 parts per million of PVP to the beer in storage may achieve further improvements in stability.

Similarly, a beverage grade of PVP K-30 is being marketed by General Aniline under the trade name Polyclar L for the clarification of wines, whiskies, vinegar, etc. In wine the complexing action of PVP becomes important in removing tannin-like materials which are introduced via the grape crushing and fermenting operations of the vintner. How PVP acts in this case will require further investigation. Possibly the PVP acts both as a complexing and flocculating agent for the haze-forming substances in the wine.

In addition to improved clarity, the use of PVP seems to reduce the harsh aftertaste of some wines. Although the PVP might be added at various stages of the process, addition after fermentation of the wine appears advantageous. No change in equipment or basic processing technique is necessary.

The optimum amount of PVP must be determined experimentally and will vary with the type of wine. Investigations conducted at the General Aniline laboratories by A. J. Martinelli show that when wine is treated with increasing amounts of Polyclar L (PVP K-30), the amount of precipitate obtained reaches a maximum at some critical value. Results with ready-for-bottling port wine (Figure 7.4) illustrate this point.

When amounts of PVP in excess of the optimum are used, a solubilizing action occurs, i.e., less precipitate is obtained. From the taste and stability observations summarized in Table 7.10, it appears that PVP should be added in amounts up to the optimum and not beyond. For port wine this would be in a range up to 4 pounds per 1000 gallons.

Similar improvements have been observed in the processing of champagne, vinegar, and some fruit juices. Investigations with straight (105 proof) whiskey indicate that as little as 40 ppm of Polyclar L can improve chill haze.

TABLE 7.9. Effect of Polyclar H on the Brewing of Beer.

Brews, 450 bbl each, treated with Polyclar H at the kettle

Brew No.	Polyclar H Addition to Wort (lb/100 bbl)	Reduction in Hops (%)	Storage Brews Ruh Storage Brews Prior to Filtration (yeast present) Appearance	Taste	Reduction in Enzymatic Chillproof (%)	Taste	Finished Brews Chill Haze (32F) (Nephelose Units) 24 hr	48 hr	Residual PVP (ppm)
1	None (control)	None	Cloudy	Harsh and bitter	None	Normal	29	28	0
2A	15	None	Less cloudy than control	Little difference from control	None	Too hoppy, ale-like	29	28	1
2B	15	None	Less cloudy than control	Little difference from control	44	Too hoppy, ale-like	23	26	<1
3A	15	15	Less cloudy than #2	Mild	None	Comparable to control	18	20	<1
3B	15	15	Less cloudy than #2	Mild	44	Comparable to control	21	23	<1
4	20	15	Least cloudy, quite clear	Definite smoothness and pleasing hop bitter	None	Smoother than control	18	20	<1

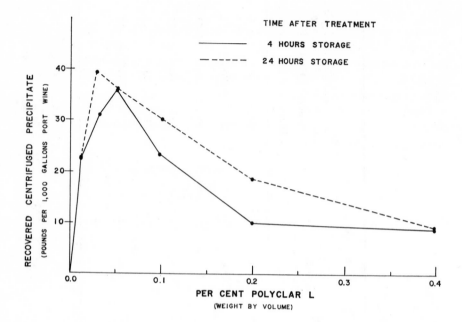

FIGURE 7.4   Precipitate formation in ready-for-bottling port wine treated with "Polyclar" L.

TABLE 7.10   Character and Stability of Ready-for-Bottling Port Wine Treated with Polyclar L.

Per Cent Polyclar L	Pounds per 1000 gal Wine	Comments on Character of Treated Port Wine	Stability 3 Months after Treatment	
			Cloudiness	Sediment
Control	—	Normal character, aroma and taste	Much	Yes
0.01	0.83	Normal character and aroma with cleaner aftertaste	Slight	Little or none
0.03	2.5	Same as 0.01%, except Port aroma slightly subdued but desirable	None	None
0.05	4.2	Same as 0.03% with "softer" taste	None	None

Detergents-Soap

Common practice in the detergent industry is to incorporate CMC into synthetic detergent formulations to act as an antisoil redeposition agent.

Although CMC gives satisfactory results on cotton, the results on other fibers are in general unsatisfactory. The protective colloid action of PVP has been compared with CMC in the General Aniline laboratories using a typical built alkyl aryl sulfonate detergent. A series of fabrics soiled with carbon black were subjected to standard Launderometer washings. The reflectance losses of the dried fabrics were measured photometrically and are given in Table 7.11. The smaller the reflectance loss is, the more effective the anti-redeposition agent.

TABLE 7.11. Comparison of PVP and CMC as Anti-redeposition Agents in an Alkyl Aryl Sulfonate Detergent.

Reflectance Loss
(Initial Reflectance Unsoiled Fabric Minus Final Reflectance)

	PVP K-15	PVP K-30	Sodium Carboxy-methylcellulose	Detergent Only
Cotton	22.4	29.7	33.0	43.8
Dacron	4.8	6.7	39.5	33.8
Nylon	26.1	31.0	62.8	63.0
Orlon	10.3	13.3	41.6	41.1
Dynel	37.0	38.8	52.5	50.6
Acetate	9.2	9.7	38.5	41.8
Rayon	31.6	36.6	51.0	59.3
Wool	5.6	6.0	15.0	15.1

Detergent Formulation
25% Sorapon* SF (85% active alkyl aryl sulfonate)
40% Sodium tripolyphosphate
28% Sodium sulfate
 6% Sodium metasilicate
 1% Anti-redeposition agent

* Registered trademark of General Aniline and Film Corporation.

While PVP shows a measurable improvement, i.e., lower reflectance loss, over CMC in cotton fabric, the effect is much more pronounced with synthetic fibers. This is significant in view of the difficulty encountered in laundering synthetic fabrics. Lowering the K-value from 30 to 15 also showed a measurable improvement. The current price ratio of PVP to CMC has limited PVP's use in this application to the fine fabrics field.

However, with the increasing use of cotton-synthetic fiber blends, the need for more effective antisoil redeposition agents will become increasingly critical. Mixtures of PVP and CMC are worthy of investigation. Another plus value which PVP offers in this field is its action as a loose-color scavenger to prevent dye migration between differently colored fabrics during laundering. PVP may be safely used in the presence of optical brightening agents.

Good results were obtained in Germany by incorporating PVP into soap and detergent bars. The effect was better bonding, especially in the case of soaps containing builders, and increased foam stability. Additions of 1 to 3 per cent PVP based on the total product were indicated (German Patent 850,328). The following example is typical:

2 parts of PVP K-90 (as a 20 per cent aqueous solution) plus
0.2 part of TiO_2 are added to
100 parts of dry soap flakes
in the amalgamator, passed through the plodders, and handled in the usual manner.

Soap in the form of films or sheets has long been recognized as a convenience from the standpoints of sanitation and disposability. Henry Goldschmiedt, writing in *Soap and Chemical Specialties*, mentions his success with a PVP-polyvinyl alcohol combination as a soap-sheet binder.

In the case of germicidal scrub soaps and detergent-sanitizing formulations, PVP can be used to reduce the skin irritation and sensitizing effects of the chlorinated phenol and bisphenol types of germicides.

Paper

In the production of fine-grade papers, a wide variety of dyed-rag stock must be stripped free of color. For white and light-toned papers this requirement is quite stringent. PVP can be used to achieve a greater degree of decolorization by addition to the basic stripping formula. The following composition is typical:

Per 1000 pounds of Rags
6 lb PVP K-30
20 lb Caustic soda
40 lb Sodium formaldehydesulfoxylate
8 lb Lignin sulfonate
Add water to give a liquor ratio of 1 to 5

A very interesting development in the field of inorganic specialty papers has been reported by T. D. Callinan as a result of investigations conducted at the Naval Research Laboratories. Using PVP, thin papers were prepared from such materials as glass fibers or mica flakes for use in filtration and electrical insulation. Handsheets were prepared by adding in sequence small amounts of aqueous PVP and aqueous PVM/MA (heteropolymer of methyl vinyl ether and maleic anhydride) to a stirred 1 per cent aqueous slurry (pH of 3) of inorganic fibers or flakes. The ratio of PVP to PVM/MA employed was about 2 to 1. Filtration through a standard sheet mold and drying of the wet web followed.

Unlike other resins studied, the PVP exerted a dispersing action, i.e., opened the stock. The PVM/MA at low pH formed a complex with the PVP and served to fix it on the inorganic surface. Seemingly polyacrylic acid could be used in place of the PVM/MA. Table 7.12 illustrates the advantages of the above technique: greatly increased tensile strength and the feasibility of preparing thin inorganic papers.

TABLE 7.12. Properties of Inorganic Papers with PVP and PVM/MA.

Stock	Made with PVP-PVM/MA			Made Without PVP-PVM/MA	
	PVP-PVM/MA (% based on paper)	Thickness (in.)	Tensile Strength (psi)	Thickness (in.)	Tensile Strength (psi)
Glass fiber A*	0.6	0.002	1200	0.025	0.01
Glass fiber AAA**	0.7	0.003	1000	0.011	40
Glass flakes	0.2	0.002	185	0.010	86
Mica flakes	2.6	0.009	160	0.040	20

* Fiber length = 1/16 to 1/8 inch; diameter = 1.25 micron.
** Fiber length = 1/128 to 1/16 inch; diameter = 0.50 micron.

Photography-Lithography

PVP is under extensive investigation in these fields in the United States. German patent literature contains references to the use of PVP in combination with light-sensitive diazo compounds for the production of deep-etch lithographic plates. The advantages claimed are uniform viscosity and storage stability. PVP may also be tanned (cross-linked) by light using the more classical ammonium dichromate.

Lithographic plates are usually stored under a thin coating of asphalt. PVP has been suggested as an intermediate coat between the plate and the asphalt to allow easy washing in preparing the plate for a press rerun.

In the preparation of photographic emulsions, the protective colloid action of PVP may be utilized as a gelatin substitute. E. K. Bolton in U.S. Patent 2,495,918 describes a method for preparing dispersions of light-sensitive silver halide grains using PVP.

Pigment and Color Dispersing

The protective colloid, solubilizing, and suspending actions of PVP may be utilized in many fields such as inks, papers, paints, as well as in pigment manufacture.

PVP is effective as a grinding aid and suspending agent with a variety of organic and inorganic pigments. Its utility will vary from pigment to pigment and must be determined experimentally using amounts in the range of 1 to 15 per cent based on the pigment.

PVP K-90 (up to 5 per cent based on the pigment) is effective as a suspending agent for TiO_2 in latex systems; it may be ground with the TiO_2 prior to addition to the latex. PVP K-15 has been found to increase the tinting strength of carbon-black dispersions at 0.5 per cent based on carbon black.

In soluble inks based on dyestuffs, PVP can improve solubility, prevent gelation, and give greater color value per pound of dyestuff. Its use in ball-point pen inks is becoming well-established. A basic ball-point pen ink formulation might include:

> 3% PVP K-30
> 32% Victoria Blue BA Base
> 65% Glycol solvent

Similarly, PVP has found use in the formulation of aqueous-based stamp-pad inks, particularly where easy washability is important.

Miscellaneous

Some of the other fields in which PVP has shown promise can be summarized briefly:

Adhesives PVP exhibits excellent adhesion to glass and many metallic and plastic surfaces. This fact coupled with its wide compatibility and solubility indicates utility in specialty adhesives. As water-soluble adhesives, various viscosity grades of PVP were marketed in Europe under the Igecoll* trademark.

Polishes In wax and polish formulations, PVP can function as a protective colloid and film former. It may be readily incorporated with many of the paste, liquid, or emulsion types to give improvements in emulsification, cleansing action, and gloss.

Polymer manufacture In the bead- or suspension-type polymerization of vinyl monomers, PVP has been reported to function as a protective colloid at concentrations of 0.5 per cent and higher based on the monomer. It has the added advantage of being compatible with most polymers so that the polymer beads obtained are clear.

FUTURE DEVELOPMENTS

Only a fraction of the market potential for PVP has been realized to date. Undoubtedly, new and unpredicted uses for this polymer will be found and

* Registered trademark of Badische Anilin und Soda Fabrik.

developed as the price of PVP is lowered. A long range price of around 70 cents a pound appears feasible.

Expanding markets in the cosmetic and pharmaceutical fields can be foreseen. Its physiological inertness in combination with its complexing action should assure PVP a place in beverage clarification. Its application in dyestuff and pigment dispersions will lead to increasing uses in the paint, ink, and paper-coating fields. Its complexing action with dyestuffs points to large markets in the synthetic fiber field as the dye-receptive ingredient. The detoxifying effect of PVP on various chemicals will be exploited to reduce the dermatological hazards of various compounded specialties which come in contact with human skin.

At this point a comment should be interjected regarding vinylpyrrolidone. This monomer offers a building block for copolymers and a means of incorporating some of the desirable properties associated with PVP into new and unique resins. Recent patent literature contains many examples of copolymers and terpolymers containing vinylpyrrolidone. Since 1956 General Aniline has marketed a series of vinylpyrrolidone-vinyl acetate copolymers. In 1961 this company introduced, under the Polectron* trademark, a group of water emulsion copolymers based on vinylpyrrolidone-styrene and vinylpyrrolidone-ethyl acrylate systems. In the same year, General Aniline introduced Polyclar AT,* a water-insoluble form of PVP, as a chill-proofing agent for beer.

Looking ahead, an interesting aspect of PVP and vinylpyrrolidone copolymers is that their potential applications are so varied and are not limited to aqueous systems.

* Registered trademark of General Aniline and Film Corporation.

F. J. Glavis

Rohm and Haas Company
Philadelphia, Pennsylvania

8

Poly(acrylic acid) and Its Homologs

Poly(acrylic acid) and other water-soluble acrylic polymers possess a wide range of physical and chemical properties which make them candidates for many applications. Extreme variations in hydrophilicity, hardness, toughness, adhesion, and complex formation constitute the basis for such wide usage. Included within the scope of this chapter are poly(acrylic acid) and poly(methacrylic acid), their salts, and copolymers of acrylic acid and methacrylic acid with hydrophobic or hydrophilic comonomers.

Many of these copolymers, either upon neutralization or other solubilizing reaction, are the base materials for much interesting chemistry and many additional applications. Outside the scope of this discussion are the many water-insoluble copolymers whose properties have been purposefully modified by the incorporation of water-soluble acrylic monomers. In these cases, necessary and useful property modifications are obtained, but water-solubility is not achieved, although variations in water sensitivity are possible. Polyacrylamide is treated elsewhere in this book (see Chapter 9).

PHYSICAL AND CHEMICAL PROPERTIES

Solid polymers derived from acrylic and methacrylic acids and their salts are hard, brittle materials with excellent clarity. A Tukon hardness rating of 40 to 50 is often found for films of such polymers, as compared with a rating of 22 for Plexiglas. Properties of such solid polymers may be readily modified by incorporation of other monomers which can reduce the Tukon hardness rating to a value of less than 5. Thus polymer properties are effectively changed by the use of a comonomer which can reduce the glass transition temperature to a desired level as indicated in Table 8.1 for copolymers of styrene and methacrylic acid in both the acid and sodium salt form (*Proceedings of the Royal Society*, A **282**, 137, Oct. 1964): Such modifying monomers may include methyl acrylate, ethyl acrylate, methyl

TABLE 8.1. Glass Transition Temperatures for Methacrylic Acid: Styrene Copolymers.

Methacrylic Acid: Styrene, Mole Per Cent	Glass Transition Temperature, C	
	Acid Form	Na-salt Form
100:0	185	. . .
40:60	175	185
20:80	150	. . .
10:90	132	143
6:94	122	120
2:98	117	120

methacrylate, higher acrylic esters, styrene, vinyl acetate, and methyl vinyl ether. A structural representation of an all-acrylic polymer is shown here.

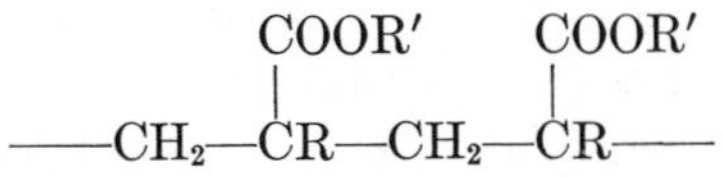

$$\begin{array}{ccc} & COOR' & COOR' \\ & | & | \\ ---CH_2-CR-CH_2-CR--- \end{array}$$

In this representation, R is H or CH_3 and R' is H, CH_3, C_2H_5, Na, K, NH_4, and the like. Such polymers exhibit various degrees of hygroscopicity and many are hydroplastic, depending upon the proportion of hydrophilic groups present in the molecule.

In the discussion which follows, solution properties of poly(acrylic acid) and poly(methacrylic acid) will be considered. Poly(acrylic acid) is a stronger acid than poly(methacrylic acid), and each polymer is a weaker acid than the corresponding monomeric acid, as indicated in the following.

Acid	pK_A*	
	monomer	polymer
Acrylic acid	4.26	4.75
Methacrylic acid	4.66	5.65

* By definition, the general form of pK reads like the pH definition ($pK = -\log k$, where k is the ionization constant). The subscript A indicates that it is the acid ionization constant. For weak acids (such as acrylic and methacrylic acids), pK equals pH at the half-neutralization point, since at this point the salt-over-acid term vanishes from the expression:

$$pK = pH + \log\left(\frac{\text{conc. acid ion}}{\text{conc. un-ionized acid}}\right)$$

With copolymers which contain acid components, it should be borne in mind that property modifications are imposed by the ionic nature of these polyelectrolytes. Often, solution behavior is further complicated by the incorporation of hydrophobic moieties in the polymer molecule.

Polymers of acrylic acid $(CH_2{=}CHCOOH)$ and methacrylic acid $[CH_2{=}C(CH_3)COOH]$ are soluble in such polar solvents as methanol, ethanol, dioxane, ethylene glycol, beta-methoxyethanol, and dimethylformamide, but are insoluble in solvents such as saturated hydrocarbons (hexane, decane), aromatic hydrocarbons (benzene, toluene), and other nonpolar solvents. Monovalent metal and ammonium salts of such polymers are generally soluble in water.

Experimental data are satisfactorily explained if it is postulated that aqueous solutions of the polyacids contain the polymer in a very slightly ionized, tightly coiled shape, with a resultant low solution viscosity. This polymer coiling can be increased and the ionization reduced if the polymer is present in dilute hydrochloric acid solution. Increasing the degree of ionization of the polymer by neutralization with a base such as sodium hydroxide results in the gradual increase of viscosity.

Data in Table 8.2 show the variation of η_{sp}/c with pH for an aqueous solution of poly(methacrylic acid) with a degree of polymerization of 2510

TABLE 8.2.   Viscosity Versus pH for Aqueous Solution of Poly (Methacrylic Acid).

pH	η_{sp}/c	
	0.172 gm/100 ml	0.011 gm/100 ml
4.0	5	5
5.8	10	10
6.0	30	30
6.2	50	50
6.3	59	—
7.0	64	240
7.5	70	—
8.3	73	255
9.0	68	200

(according to data of Katchalsky and Eisenberg). It can be seen that as sodium hydroxide is added, the value of the specific viscosity over concentration is increased, but that as the sodium hydroxide is added in excess, this value is reduced. These effects are accentuated at lower polymer concentrations.

In the presence of hydrochloric acid solution, ionization of the polyacid is apparently reduced from its initial low value, and the polymer formed presumably possesses a nonpermeable, coiled configuration. With the first increment of neutralizing base, some ionization occurs, providing sodium counterions and the polymeric ion. As more and more of the carboxyl groups on the polymer chain become ionized, mutual repulsion of the charges forces the polymer chain to uncoil and assume a more nearly rodlike configuration with a resultant increased resistance to flow and increased solution viscosity. After complete neutralization has been achieved, the addition of more sodium hydroxide results in a buildup of sodium counter-ions and hence a repression of the effective ionization of the polymer chain. The effect is some chain coiling and a consequent reduction in solution viscosity.

More recent work shows evidence for conformational change in the poly-(methacrylic acid) molecule in the neighborhood of about 20 per cent neutralization. This conformational change is attributed to intrachain attractive forces, hydrophobic bonding of the pendant methyl group, or effect of dielectric constant of or counter-ion concentration in immediately adjacent water molecules. The change is evidenced by discontinuities at this critical interval in the degree of neutralization in potentiometric titration curves, far ultraviolet absorption spectra, plots of specific viscosity against concentration, acridine orange dye binding, and spectral perturbations with inserted hydrophobic chromophore groups (*Journal of Macromolecular Chemistry*, **1**, 291, no. 2, 1966).

When observed at all, such conformational change for poly(acrylic acid) is much less marked than for the methacrylic acid analogs (*Journal of Polymer Science*, A **3**, 2555, 1965). Also ascribed to similar attractive forces and the resultant shorter statistical chain element of poly(methacrylic acid) is the negative heat and entropy of dilution, as contrasted with poly(acrylic acid) — (Eliasef, *Journal of Polymer Science*, B **3**, 767, 1965).

The solution properties of such polyacids are therefore affected by the strength of the acid, degree of ionization, kind and amount of counter-ion, and the concentration of the polymer in solution. Polymer-polymer interactions can further complicate the picture by such phenomena as hydrogen bonding, attractive forces, and steric effects.

A comparison of the acid strength of poly(acrylic acid) with various copolymers of acrylic acid and acrylamide has shown that the acid strength of the block copolymer is the same as that of a linear homopolymer of acrylic acid. In contrast, a random copolymer exhibits greater acid strength and graft and branched copolymers show weaker strengths than the linear homopolymer.

A graphic demonstration of the postulated coiling and uncoiling of polyacids has been developed by Katchalsky. He obtained mechanical work from strips of poly(methacrylic acid) by changing the ionic atmosphere in the solution in which the polymer strip is suspended while attached at each end to a device for measuring mechanical work. Ion atmosphere changes result in alternate contraction and stretching of the polymer strip. Similar tieno or pH muscle effects have been reported for specific physical mixtures of poly(acrylic acid) and polyvinyl alcohol (Walters, Kuhn, and Kuhn, *Nature*, **189**, 381, 1962) and similar fibers with a central platinum counter-electrode (*Nature*, **206**, 1149, 1965). Interactions of the polymeric acids with alkylene oxide polymers have also been reported (Smith, Winslow, and Petersen, *Industrial & Engineering Chemistry*, **51**, 1361, 1959).

The nature of the counter-ion has been investigated extensively. In addition to the repression of coiling by mass effects of excess counter-ions, certain ions can form complexes with polyions. For example, copper ions form an insoluble complex with the polyacrylate ion. The effect of polyvalent counter-ions thus may be one of mass law repression or of insoluble complex formation. Transport of an electric current by a variety of counter-ions has shown that with each kind of counter-ion, certain proportions are bound to the polyion, while the remainder are present as freely moving single ion species.

Clearly, the determination of such properties as electric anisotropy, streaming birefringence, and molecular weight are greatly affected by the ambient ionic atmosphere in which such determinations are made. Molecular weights have been determined by light-scattering techniques in hydrochloric acid solution, and reasonable agreement of values has been obtained viscometrically. The molecular weight of poly(sodium acrylate) has been determined by osmometric methods using an external medium of sodium chloride solution to compensate for the Donnan term in the dialysis.

What appears to be the most satisfactory method for determining the molecular weight, however, consists of converting the polyacid to the corresponding methyl ester by reaction with diazomethane, and then determining the molecular weight of the formed ester by more reliable methods. Katchalsky and Eisenberg have demonstrated that no change in molecular weight takes place in this esterification step. In the course of this and subsequent Japanese work, it was further brought out that no molecular weight degradation results from hydrolysis of the polymeric methyl ester to the acid with either aqueous sodium hydroxide or p-toluene sulfonic acid in aqueous acetic acid.

Other workers have derived expressions for the molecular weight of polyacids from viscometric analysis in various solvent media designed to eliminate the effect of ionization of the polyelectrolyte. In Table 8.3 are listed the polymer, solvent, and k and α values to be used in the calculation of the molecular weight from the formula: intrinsic viscosity $= kM^{\alpha}$, in

TABLE 8.3. Data for Molecular Weight Determinations.

Polymer	Solvent	k	α	Temperature, C
Poly(acrylic acid)	Dioxane	85×10^{-5}	0.5	30
Poly(methacrylic acid)	$2M$ NaNO$_3$ solution	49.4×10^{-5}	0.65	25
Poly(methacrylic acid)	$0.002M$ HCl solution	66×10^{-4}	0.5	30
Poly(methacrylic acid)	Methanol	2.42×10^{-3}	0.51	26

which M is the molecular weight, and intrinsic viscosity is in units of deciliters per gram.

While conventional poly(acrylic acid) is soluble in both water and acetic acid, evidence is now available to suggest that isotactic poly(acrylic acid) is insoluble in these solvents. The hydrolysis of conventional and syndiotactic poly(isopropyl acrylate) in aqueous acetic acid medium with p-toluene sulfonic acid results in the formation of a water-soluble poly(acrylic acid). On the other hand, a similar hydrolysis of isotactic polymer produces a poly(acrylic acid) which is insoluble in both water and aqueous acetic acid.

It is thus strongly suggested that the hydrolysis of the isotactic polymer has been accomplished without destroying polymer tacticity, and that isotactic poly(acrylic acid) has indeed been produced by this method. By a heterogeneous hydrolysis technique, stereospecific copolymers of methyl methacrylate and sodium methacrylate have been produced. Solution properties of such tactic polyacids appear to be different from those of conventional polymers.

Crystalline poly(acrylic acid), identified by X-ray and electron microscopy, has been obtained by the hydrolysis of *tert*-butyl acrylate polymer of definite tactic form (Miller, Botty, and Rauhet, *Journal of Colloid Science*, **15**, 83, 1960). To demonstrate the specific effect of tactic form upon the capacity for the polymer to participate in reactions, it has been shown at the University of Tokyo that isotactic poly(methacrylic acid) is the most active tactic form in the mutarotation of α-D-glucose (*Polymer Report*, **96**, 19, 1966).

Aqueous solutions of poly(methacrylic acid) of sufficiently high molecular weight have been reported to possess negative thixotropy. In these cases, agitation of the solution results in a marked increase in apparent viscosity, and this effect appears to be reversible.

METHODS OF PREPARATION

Poly(acrylic acid) and its homologs may be prepared by direct polymerization of the appropriate monomer. A conventional polymerization recipe involves water, acrylic acid monomer, potassium persulfate as the polymerization initiator, and such an activator as sodium thiosulfate. Such polymerizations may be carried out at a temperature of 50 to 100C. To regulate the polymer chain length, a number of chain transfer systems have been used. These include secondary alcohols, mercaptosuccinic acid, and combinations of sodium hypophosphite and copper acetate. The solution viscosity of such linear polymers is a direct function of the molecular weight of the polymer. Similar polymerizations in aqueous solutions have also been carried out by irradiation of the aqueous solutions with ultraviolet light; very high molecular weights are produced by this technique.

Both acrylic acid and methacrylic acid have been polymerized by dissolving the monomeric acid in a solvent, such as benzene, heating the solution in the presence of an initiator, such as benzoyl peroxide, and removing the insoluble polymer formed by filtration. Still another technique involves the formation of a slurry from preformed polymeric acid and more of the same monomer, treatment with a polymerization initiator, and conversion to a solid polymer by the application of heat. No additional solvent is employed in this reaction.

Monomeric acids have also been polymerized by exposing the monomers to Co^{60} radiation. The polymer is presumably formed by a free-radical mechanism, and the polymer continues to form for long time intervals following the cessation of irradiation. This subsequent polymerization is probably initiated by the trapped, free radicals. Polymer has been formed in this way from frozen methacrylic acid; and nuclear magnetic resonance studies suggest the presence of a completely atactic configuration.

Salts of acrylic and methacrylic acids may also be polymerized by treatment with initiators in aqueous media. Pinner has reported data which show that the methacrylate ion polymerizes at a rate which is lower than that at which the un-ionized acid polymerizes, but there are numerous techniques which employ the polymerization of the monomeric salt as the means of obtaining the polymer. The polymerization of a concentrated paste of an acrylic salt in the presence of a carbonate has been described for the preparation of a readily pulverizable polymeric cake. It has also been reported that acrylic salts have been polymerized successfully by gamma-ray irradiation.

Because of the nonvolatility of the acrylic salts, certain specialized techniques have been developed for their polymerization. Simultaneous polymerization and spray drying have been employed to produce relatively high molecular weight polymers from initially water-thin, concentrated, monomer feed stocks. A similar technique has been employed for the simultaneous drum drying and polymerization of acrylic salts. The use of such materials as polyethylene glycol monolaurate has been described for making a drum-dried polymer more readily pulverizable.

Both acrylic and methacrylic anhydride have been polymerized to produce what are believed to be cyclo, intra-intersoluble polymers.

In addition to the polymerization of the appropriate monomer, the hydrolysis of a suitable polymer constitutes a major method of preparation of both the polymeric acid and salt. To produce poly(sodium acrylate), saponification may be carried out by heating a suspension or an emulsion of a polymeric acrylic ester, such as methyl acrylate, with aqueous sodium hydroxide at 100C for a few hours. The formed alkanol can be removed by stripping operations.

Similarly, treatment of polymeric acrylamide or acrylonitrile with alkali results in the formation of the polymeric salt. The course of the reaction is suggested in the following scheme, in which R represents a polymeric backbone, and the functional grouping is intended to be repeated along this backbone. It is readily seen that partial hydrolysis will result in the formation of copolymers:

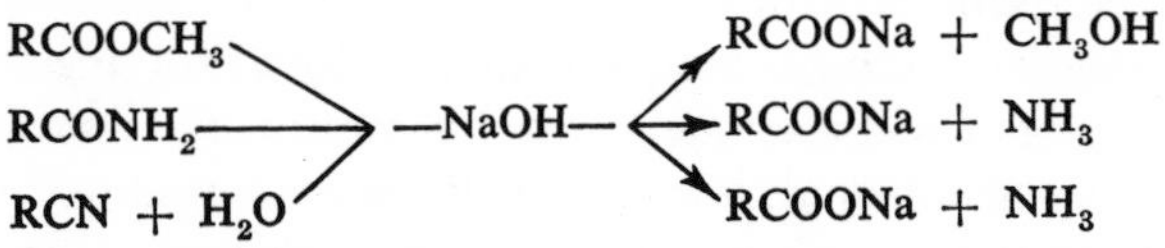

$$
\begin{array}{l}
\text{RCOOCH}_3 \\
\text{RCONH}_2 \\
\text{RCN} + \text{H}_2\text{O}
\end{array}
\Big\rangle \longrightarrow -\text{NaOH}- \Big\langle
\begin{array}{l}
\text{RCOONa} + \text{CH}_3\text{OH} \\
\text{RCOONa} + \text{NH}_3 \\
\text{RCOONa} + \text{NH}_3
\end{array}
$$

In addition to the above hydrolyses, conducted in aqueous media to produce aqueous concentrates of the desired polymeric salt, slurry hydrolyses have been reported. These are carried out in the presence of minor amounts of organic solvents, or even in the absence of such a solvent, with the products obtained in a granular, solid form. By means of an aqueous alcoholic medium, polymers with 50 or more per cent acrylonitrile content have been hydrolyzed with caustic so that the final hydrolysate is insoluble in the alcoholic reaction medium and can be removed by filtration.

The relative ease of hydrolysis of the acrylate ester polymers has not been found to hold with the corresponding methacrylate esters (Bevington, Eaves, and Vale, *Journal of Polymer Science*, **32**, 317, 1958). Recent quantitative studies have corroborated earlier findings that conventional methods produce complete hydrolysis of poly(methyl acrylate) while, under the same conditions, no appreciable hydrolysis of poly(methyl methacrylate) is obtained.

Hydrolyses of the methacrylate polymers have recently been accomplished to produce poly(sodium methacrylate). A technique involving molten caustic and another method employing aqueous isopropanol and sodium hydroxide in a heterogeneous system were used. In addition to the different hydrolysis rates for acrylates and methacrylates, a markedly different rate has also been demonstrated for conventional, syndiotactic, and isotactic poly(methyl methacrylate), with the latter hydrolyzed at a much more rapid rate than the others (U.S. Patent 3,029,228, Apr. 10, 1962, F. J. Glavis).

Hydrolyses have also been carried out on copolymers, with the component monomers individually hydrolyzable, or with one or more of the monomers not susceptible to hydrolysis. On the other hand, hydrolysis of a homopolymer has been conducted with mixtures of bases, i.e., sodium hydroxide and calcium hydroxide, to produce double salts.

The preparation of acidic polymers by hydrolysis can be conducted by saponification, as described above, followed by removal of the counter-ions. This removal has been carried out by means of dialysis, although complete removal of cations by this procedure is difficult. An alternative method is the use of a mixed-bed, ion-exchange resin which will remove the counter-ions and any contaminant monomeric anions while leaving the polymeric acid in solution. The treatment can be carried out by column techniques or by agitation of the solid resin with the polymer solution, with subsequent removal of the resin by filtration.

Acid hydrolysis may be carried out directly by dissolving the polymeric ester in a solution of acetic acid and water in a ratio of about 80 to 20. After solution has been completed, p-toluene sulfonic acid is added and the batch heated to 110 to 120C, while passing a stream of nitrogen through the solution and removing formed alkyl acetate. The polymer may be isolated by precipitation techniques

With increased amounts of p-toluene sulfonic acid and with increased hydrolysis time, it has been found possible to hydrolyze methyl methacrylate polymer by this technique, especially isotactic poly(methyl methacrylate) which can be hydrolyzed completely. Hydrolysis of the polymeric esters has also been accomplished by dissolving the polymer in concentrated sulfuric acid, warming, and isolating the product by pouring the reaction mixture into water.

The preparation of copolymers can be carried out to produce soluble or solubilizable types. Soluble copolymers can be produced by copolymerization of hydrophilic monomers. For instance, acrylic acid and/or methacrylic acid have been copolymerized with maleic anhydride, itaconic acid, acrylamide, sodium salts of acrylic or methacrylic acids, and methyl vinyl ether to produce water-soluble polymers. Water-soluble polymers have also been produced by partial hydrolysis of polymeric esters, amides, and nitriles, or by co-hydrolysis with mixed bases. Depending upon the monomer employed, it is also possible to prepare soluble copolymers with small amounts of hydrophobic monomers.

Solubilizable copolymers have been prepared by solution, emulsion, and suspension techniques from blends of acrylic and methacrylic acid with larger amounts of hydrophobic monomers. For instance, copolymers prepared from 65 per cent methyl methacrylate and 35 per cent methacrylic acid are water-insoluble, but aqueous suspensions or emulsions of such copolymers are readily solubilized by the addition of such bases as ammonium hydroxide or sodium hydroxide.

The preparation of polyampholytes from acrylic monomers has been reported. Such polyampholytes have been produced from dimethylaminoethyl methacrylate and methacrylic acid in various ratios (Doty, *Journal of the American Chemical Society*, **76**, 3764, 1954). Another class of polyampholytes has been prepared from acrylic acid and vinylpyridine. These polymers can be quaternized with alkyl bromides, and when mixtures of bromides such as ethyl and dodecyl are employed, the interesting polysoaps are formed. They are effective surfactants by virtue of possessing hydrophilic and hydrophobic moieties in the same molecule.

POLYMER REACTIONS

Neutralization

Neutralization of polymeric acids has been accomplished with a variety of bases. Of the inorganic class, monovalent and polyvalent bases have been employed. In the case of polymeric salts with both monovalent and polyvalent counter-ions, several effects are produced. When counter-ions are in excess of stoichiometry, both repression of effective ionization, resulting in viscosity decrease, and salting-out of the polymer are encountered.

In both instances, isolation of the polymer and separation from the excess counter-ions present permit resolubilization of the formed salt in fresh water. In other cases, such as with copper ions, complex formation occurs; the precipitated polymer salt here cannot be redissolved. This complex formation is so rapid that actual fibers of the copper salt of poly(acrylic acid) can be formed by introducing a thin filament of an aqueous solution of the sodium salt of the polymer into a solution of copper chloride. As suggested earlier, this binding of counter-ions takes place in different degrees with the different ions employed for the neutralization.

An extension of this idea is the formation of the zinc-ammonium or zirconium-ammonium salt of an acrylic polyacid. Such a salt is water-soluble. Upon drying down a film formed from an aqueous solution of such a polymer, the ammonia is lost with the water during evaporation, and the residual polyvalent metal salt of the polyacid is extremely resistant to attack by water. Werner complexes of chromium with poly(acrylic acid) may also be used to form insoluble residues.

The formation of double salts by neutralization with mixed bases has been mentioned previously. Similarly, the *in situ* formation of insoluble salts may be used in cases requiring the introduction of a soluble form of the polymer for maximum penetration, but insolubilization *in situ* in order to achieve a desired degree of impenetrability. A case in point is the introduction of calcium chloride solution into a previously impregnated formation in which the impregnant was poly(acrylic acid).

Organic bases may also be used for the neutralization step, especially in those cases in which modifications in film properties or polymer solubility are desired. Representative neutralizing organic bases include triethylamine, tri(hydroxyethyl)amine, tetramethylammonium hydroxide, morpholine, and choline. Polyfunctional amines may also be used.

In this latter category, polymeric bases have been used to produce insoluble films. Representative polymers are those derived from acrylic acid and from dimethylaminoethyl methacrylate.

Reversal of neutralization is often desired. For this purpose, dialysis has been employed, but as suggested earlier, the complete removal of cations is difficult by this means. Alternatively, ion-exchange resins have been employed, especially in small-scale operations. With an appropriate cation-exchange resin, column techniques have been used to prepare poly(acrylic acid) from its soluble salts.

A wide variation has been noted in the base used for the neutralization operation, and as already indicated, the same wide latitude exists in the choice of the acidic polymer. By variation in the hydrophobic component of the polymer molecule, it is possible to provide water-soluble polymer compositions which will form films or other final shapes which have a wide range of physical properties involving resolubility of the film, hardness, toughness, gloss, clarity, and other features.

Esterification

Esterification of the polymeric acids has been carried out by the preparation of the silver salt and subsequent reaction with the appropriate alkyl halide. A more convenient method of preparation is that involving the use of diazomethane or diazoethane. Suspension of the polyacid in a benzene solution of the diazo compound results in the evolution of nitrogen and the gradual solution of the polymeric ester in the solvent from which it can be removed by conventional techniques.

Esterification is also conducted by treatment of the polyacid with an alcohol at elevated temperatures. This has been used with glycols and glycerine to induce cross-linking and insolubilization of films of poly(acrylic acid), especially in the formation of a durable finish for textile-sizing application.

Still another ester-forming reaction is that involving an alkylene oxide. The polymeric acids and their salts have been treated with alkylene oxides to produce polymeric esters by the following reaction:

$$-CH_2-CHCOOH-CH_2-CHCOOH- \quad + \quad CH_2-CH_2 \longrightarrow$$
$$\text{O}$$

$$-CH_2-CH(COOCH_2CH_2OH)-CH_2-CH(COOCH_2CH_2OH)-$$

With such catalysts as piperidine or sodium hydroxide, the reaction is reported to proceed smoothly; and the beta-hydroxyethyl ester has sites for the further reaction of alkylene oxide groups, resulting in the formation of grafted polyoxyethylene side chains on a backbone of poly(acrylic acid). The likelihood of cross-linking and insolubilization by interaction between terminal hydroxyl groups and acidic portions of other polymer chains offers an opportunity for controlled film insolubilization.

Conditions have been reported for control of the preparation of the alkylene oxide adducts to avoid premature insolubilization by interchain reactions. This involves the continuous adjustment of the pH of the reaction medium and a careful regulation of the ratio of the alkylene oxide to the poly(acrylic acid). The reaction should be conducted at a temperature of about 100C.

Complex Formation

An association complex of poly(acrylic acid) with polyethers, such as polyoxyethylene glycols, has been reported. This complex forms readily at ordinary temperatures and appears to involve formation of strong hydrogen bonds. The resultant products are tough, hard, and water-insoluble. Possibly similar complexes of poly(acrylic acid) with poly(N-vinylpyrrolidone) have also been made.

Another complex has been reported between poly(acrylic acid) and clays of various kinds. There is no doubt that stable aggregates can be formed by mixing such a polyacid with soil. The mechanism of such an aggregate stabilization may involve the formation of stable complexes at various sites of soil particles at different points on an extended polymer chain, thus effectively holding together groups of the individual particles.

A reaction complex has also been found to exist between nylon and poly-(acrylic acid). When the latter is used as a sizing agent for nylon, and the bulk of the nylon is dissolved away from the sized fiber, a network of nylon to which the poly(acrylic acid) is spot-welded remains.

Other Reactions

Heating a mixture of poly(acrylic acid) with a polyamine such as tetra-ethylenepentamine results in the formation of substituted amides. The formation of a hydrazide, hydrazone, and azide from poly(acrylic acid) has also been observed.

What may be a fairly complicated series of reactions involves the polymerization of a basic monomer such as dimethylaminoethyl methacrylate in the presence of preformed poly(acrylic acid). This reaction could involve polymer grafting or a neutralization of the polyacid by the monomeric base with polymerization of the pendant monomer function. The possibility of homopolymer formation with subsequent mutual neutralization by the acidic and basic polymers should not be excluded.

APPLICATIONS

The multiplicity of applications of poly(acrylic acid) and other water-soluble acrylic polymers is the direct result of the varied physical properties and many polymer reactions noted previously. Many of the applications depend on the ability of these polymers to form complexes, and the bonding action to such substrates opens up additional fields of use.

The clarity, toughness, and durability of the polymers lead to still other end uses. While many of the applications described here are not clearly understood, it is possible that more than one of the properties or reactions of the polymers are involved in the successful applications.

Thickeners

Latex thickeners   The thickening of polymer latex systems is required for a wide variety of applications. The mechanism of this thickening action is not clearly understood, although several mechanisms might be expected as a result of the wide range of water-soluble polymers and polymer latexes involved. Garret and Brown (*Journal of Applied Polymer Science*, **1**, No. 3, 287–295, 1959) have suggested that this complex phenomenon involves the ability of a water-soluble polymer to thicken the aqueous phase of the polymer latex, to interact with the polymer to produce a pseudo-aggregate of polymer particles, and to interact with emulsifiers and other ingredients of the latex.

Water-soluble acrylic polymers are effective latex thickeners. With any given water-soluble polymer, thickening of the latex is increased with increased molecular weight of the thickener, which indicates some support for the requirement of thickening the aqueous phase. However, very low molecular weight polymers, which have a relatively small thickening effect in water, may be extremely effective in thickening certain latexes.

This variability of thickening action is typical and may be attributed to the various latex compositions, particularly the nature of the emulsifier. The phenomenon is made even more complex with compounded latex formulations in which the thickener may also react with clay, pigments, and fillers introduced into the system.

In handling certain rubber latexes, especially natural rubber, a convenient practice is to cream the latex in order to concentrate the rubber. The addition of such a creaming agent as a low molecular weight sodium salt of poly(acrylic acid) to a 40 per cent natural rubber latex will result in the separation into a clear serum layer and a more concentrated, approximately 60 per cent latex layer.

In textile applications, the thickening of latexes is required in the backing of rugs for the preparation of resilient, rubberized, nonslip floor coverings. It is also used in upholstery fabric backing. Thickened latexes are also required for dipping operations in which fabric forms may be dipped in thickened rubber latex and the covered form cured to prepare such articles as gloves.

The latex paint field is a rapidly expanding one. The adjustment of such paints to a desired viscosity level is required for brushing and roller and spray application. Viscosity adjustment can be made with water-soluble acrylics. In addition, the final formulation must be stable. Both formulation stability and reduction of viscosity drift of the thickened paint are achieved with selected acrylic thickeners. They also serve as grinding media for the preparation of paint pastes.

Nonflammable hydraulic fluids   There is a real interest in the development of a nonflammable fluid for use in power transmission and actuating devices. Such hydraulic fluids find use in such industrial establishments as foundries. In these cases, since the fluids are under considerable pressure, a leak or rupture in the lines results in the formation of a fine mist of a potentially flammable material, if the base for the fluid is a petroleum lubricant or other flammable stock.

One method of reducing the danger of such fires has been the use of blends of water with ethylene glycol. In order to improve the lubricity of such systems and to adjust their viscosity to the desired level, water-soluble acrylic polymers have been employed. Polymer modification or the addition of antitack agents is required to prevent the formation of hard films at valve fittings, such as would be formed by poly(sodium acrylate).

Viscous flooding   In the secondary recovery of underground petroleum deposits, it is customary to employ flooding techniques. In this operation, an injection well is drilled in a central location in which it is surrounded by producing wells. Water is then injected underground, and this water flood forces the petroleum deposits out toward the producing wells with consequent increase in oil recovery.

Success has been achieved in the addition of surface-active agents to such flooding waters. In certain cases, however, where the petroleum crudes are more viscous, the flooding water is incapable of forcing the heavier material ahead of it, and the deposit is merely channeled. Some evidence is suggested for the use of water-soluble polymers for the thickening of flooding waters to overcome this difficulty. Such viscous flooding studies have included water-soluble acrylic polymers.

The requirements for these polymers are that efficient thickening be achieved at very low polymer concentrations and that this thickening be affected relatively little by dissolved salts and brackish water. Modifications of poly(acrylic acid) are therefore necessary to overcome its known susceptibility to insolubilization with polyvalent metal ions.

Miscellaneous The extent of thickening applications may be suggested by the following representative uses. In textile operations thickening of printing pastes has been carried out with the water-soluble acrylic polymers. Ceramic glazes have been thickened for use as patching compositions, and the thickener subsequently burned off. Jelly toothpaste and shaving cream have been bodied with such polymers. Stabilization of ice cream with alkali metal (sodium) salts of poly(acrylic acid) has been claimed.

Suspending and Dispersing Agents

Petroleum production One method of drilling for petroleum deposits involves the use of drilling muds. The well is drilled with a bit, the shaft of which is increased in length, as the hole deepens, by adding sections. As each section is added, a section of pipe is also put in place around the shaft so that the drilling mud can be pumped down around the shaft to lubricate and clean the drilling bit. In returning to the surface via the annulus, the mud also carries cuttings to the surface.

In the preparation of the muds, clays in various formulations are customarily used. The upgrading of such muds can be accomplished by the use of poly(acrylic acid) or its homologs. Such upgrading results in the formation of more barrels of mud from a given quantity of ingredients.

Two other drilling applications will be mentioned here, although the action of such an additive as poly(acrylic acid) or other water-soluble acrylic polymers is more complex than that of a mere suspending agent. If the drilling mud passes through a porous structure in the underground formation as it returns to the surface, appreciable water loss results. This leads to deterioration of the formation and to the loss of raw materials. Fluid-loss additives are employed to seal up such porous formations and thus prevent this loss.

Large quantities of starch and carboxymethylcellulose are used for this operation. As drilling has proceeded to deeper and deeper levels, bacterial and thermal degradation have suggested the use of less susceptible fluid-loss additives. Hydrolyzed polyacrylonitrile has been used and has been able to withstand both bacterial and thermal conditions. However, the susceptibility to insolubilization by polyvalent metal ions has limited its usefulness in this application.

A related problem involves the prevention of water intake when the core passes through an underground deposit of water-bearing sands. Such water shut-off has been effected by either polymer insolubilization or *in situ* polymerization.

Metal production   In the preparation of copper pellets, poly-(acrylic acid) serves as both a dispersant and an activator for the reduction of the copper. In addition, the particle size of the copper pellets is controlled by the same additive.

Poly(acrylic acid) is also said to be advantageous in nickel-plating processes, presumably by virtue of dispersant activity.

Dispersancy   Poly(acrylic acid) and certain of its derivatives serve as effective dispersants, primarily for inorganic pigments. For this purpose polymers of low molecular weight are preferred. Their use includes paint applications, in which improved homogeneity and stability of formulations is achieved, presumably by interaction of the polymer with sites on the suspended pigments or fillers. Use in adhesive formulations, automotive polishes, and cleaners follows the same pattern. Organic pigments are not dispersed effectively. However, the lack of foaming in dispersed formulations in many cases offsets this restricted activity.

A fluidity titration procedure has been reported for determining dispersing activity. This procedure consists of titrating a nonfluid slurry of the pigment and extenders to be dispersed with small increments of a 10 per cent dispersant solution and recording an arbitrary fluidity end point at which it is assumed the pigment is dispersed. In Table 8.4 are listed the amounts of low molecular weight poly(sodium acrylate) which are required to disperse the designated pigments.

Miscellaneous   Poly(acrylic acid) and certain derivatives have been used as additives for boiler-feed water. In this case, they are reported to act as suspending agents for the developed boiler scale, allowing longer operating time between shutdowns for boiler cleanup and greater efficiency of heat transfer.

In many polmerization processes, a dispersing agent is required to main-

TABLE 8.4.   Fluidity Titrations for Determining Dispersing Activity.

Pigment	Weight Per Cent Dispersant on Pigment	Weight Per Cent Pigment Concentration
BaSO$_4$	0.086–0.11	77
ZnO	0.11–0.14	69
Fe$_2$O$_3$	0.14–0.17	58
Kaolin	0.086–0.11	70
CaCO$_3$	0.04–0.06	71
Carbon black	8+	21 max.

tain the initial monomer charge and the ultimate polymer particles in a relatively stable latex form. For this purpose, such derivatives as the ammonium salt of poly(methacrylic acid) have been reported effective.

Flocculants

A great variety of water-soluble polymers function as flocculants for many types of suspended materials. Polymers which have been used in this type of application include cationic, anionic, and neutral molecules derived from such monomers as dimethylaminoethyl methacrylate, acrylic acid, and acrylamide, respectively. Because of the divergence of base materials and effective polymer types, the action is not explained by a simple mechanism. It has been suggested that best results may come with the use of a fairly long-chain, linear polymer. This functions to encompass a number of the individual fine particles of the dispersed material, attaching itself to the particles at various sites by means of chemical bonds, electrostatic attraction, or other attractive forces. Relatively stable aggregates are thus produced.

Clarification   Flocculants have been used to clarify a number of liquids which have suspended fines contaminating them. Such aggregated materials may be removed by filtration, settling, or other convenient means. Acrylic polymers, such as poly(sodium acrylate), have been reported of interest in water clarification and in the treatment of sugar solutions. Fields of application include white water treatment in paper manufacture and sewage disposal problems.

Metallurgy   The water-soluble acrylic polymers have found application in the recovery of ores from suspension in water. In addition to the clarification of the water, a further object in metallurgical processes is to recover the aggregated ore fines. The increased speed of settling and the enhanced rate of filtration are responsible for the successful application of these polymers to this type of operation.

This type of aggregation to improve settling and/or filtration rates has been expanded to include other than metallurgical fines. For instance, in the filtration of a precipitate such as calcium sulfate, improved filtration rates are obtained by prior flocculation with such polymers as the acrylics.

Soil conditioning A few years ago, appreciable publicity was given to synthetic soil conditioners, materials designed to make stable aggregates in soil to improve the tilth of the soil and plant germination, and to reduce water loss from the soil and runoff of top soil in heavy rains. The inability of these polymers to compete economically with other methods of soil treatment does not alter the fact that they do indeed function as very efficient stabilization agents for soil aggregates. Table 8.5 shows data which support this statement.

TABLE 8.5.   Aggregate Stability with Hydrolyzed Polyacrylonitrile.

| Soil Type | Per Cent of Soil Weight Finer than 0.006 mm | | |
	0.00 gm polymer per 100 gm soil	0.05 gm polymer per 100 gm soil	0.10 gm polymer per 100 gm soil
Virginia sandy clay	15.5	0.0	0.0
New Hampshire silt	65.0	0.0	0.0
Texas alkali sand	37.4	6.1	9.4

Data reported from *Agricultural and Food Chemistry*, **1**, 13, 835 (September 16, 1953).

Although many successful field trials were run suggesting that improved soil performance was obtained for certain treated plots as compared with untreated controls, the stabilization effect is readily noted by first forming soil aggregates in the laboratory, treating them with an aqueous solution of the polymer in question, and then placing the aggregates on the top screen of a set of screens of progessively decreasing opening size, and then jigging the assembly while it is immersed in water. After a given time, the loss in particle stability is observed by noting the amount of soil retained on each of the screens in the assembly.

This demonstrated aggregate stabilizing effect has also been suggested for application in erosion control on roadside banks, railroad rights of way, and temporary construction operations.

In contrast to this type of effect, actual soil stabilization, i.e., the more durable hardening and impermeabilization of soil structures such as walls and dikes, has been achieved by the *in situ* polymerization of soluble acrylic derivatives, such as blended calcium acrylate and methylene bisacrylamide.

Binders

In certain applications, it is necessary to impart green strength to molded articles so that they may retain reasonable dimensional stability after formation in a wet condition until they have been fired or cured to their final form. For convenience, the temporary binder employed for this purpose should be capable of being burned out during the firing operation. Operations requiring such temporary binders include ceramic manufacture, asbestos-board preparation, and the formation of vitreous grinding wheels. A specific use is the formation of nickel briquettes in which poly(acrylic acid) is especially effective.

Coatings

Textile sizes In the textile operations of weaving and knitting, it is often desirable to size the yarn or thread. This is done to reduce machine shutdowns resulting from fouling of the shuttles and other working parts with fuzzballs formed by loose ends and fibrillation of the fiber. Sizing is accomplished by passing the thread through an aqueous bath containing the agent and thus placing a coating on the outside of the fiber.

After drying, the fiber can be woven or knitted, and the size can then be removed by washing, or it may be left on the fabric as a temporary finish or feel-improver. Starch is widely used in the sizing of cotton. Blends of salts of poly(acrylic acid) with starch find application in this and finishing operations by virtue of a plasticizing action imparted to the starch.

With nylon and other synthetic fibers, such as Dacron, sizing has been most effectively carried out with poly(acrylic acid) or other suitable water-soluble acrylic polymers. Poly(acrylic acid), as suggested earlier, is apparently spot-welded to the nylon and thus serves as an effective sizing agent, which may be readily removed by subsequent washing techniques. Alternatively, a durable finish can be achieved by heat curing the polyacid, with or without added glycerine or polyhydroxy compound, before it has been removed.

Leather finishing In the finishing of leather, base and top coats are applied in order to improve the appearance, feel, durability, and general performance of the leather article. Water-soluble acrylic polymers have been suggested for application as pigment binders and clear top-coat vehicles in the formulation of such finishing systems.

Paints In addition to the previously mentioned use as binders and dispersants in paint formulations, certain acrylic polymers may offer possibilities as paint vehicles. These are the zinc-ammonium and zirconium-ammonium salts of acrylic acid polymers which operate by virtue of the loss of ammonia during the volatilization of the water and drying of the film. Other volatile neutralizing bases may also be used, i.e., morpholine.

Paper The use of poly(acrylic acid) and some of its derivatives has been suggested for slush-stock or beater-additive application for the improvement of suspending properties in the stock or performance properties, i.e., dry strength, of the formed paper.

Lithographic printing mats have been prepared with the ammonium salt of poly(acrylic acid) applied as a coating on the paper. After suitable treatment, the mat retains a proper combination of ink holdout and rewet properties to function satisfactorily in this application.

Cosmetics The water-soluble acrylic polymers are of interest in hair-finishing formulations in which they serve to coat the hair and permit setting and styling operations.

Film formation The use of poly(acrylic acid) as a film former has been directed toward many applications. Representative of this type is the suggested use of the sodium salt of poly(acrylic acid) as the major component of a nonglare coating for headlights.

Leather Paste

When animal hides have been unhaired, tanned, and washed, they are customarily dried by placing them on vertical panels which then move slowly through a drying tunnel. This operation requires several hours. The hides may be tacked peripherally to the panels; but drying shrinks the hides, which thus may pull away from the tacks and rip the edges in so doing.

It has become more desirable to paste the hides to the drying panels. This procedure requires a paste possessing good wet adhesion in order to prevent dropoff of hides in the drying tunnel. The paste must also have relatively poor dry adhesion so that the hides can be readily removed from the panels at the end of the operation without damaging the grain of the hide; and it must be readily removed from the dried hide by brushing or swabbing. Water-soluble acrylic polymers have found use in this paste application, either alone or in conjunction with starch or carboxymethylcellulose.

Ion-Exchange Resins

Water solubility of an acrylic polyacid can be reduced either by reducing the acid content of a copolymer with a hydrophobic comonomer, or by cross-linking the acid polymer. In the latter case, complete water insolubility can be achieved. Such insoluble polyacids constitute a major group among the ion-exchange resins.

CONCLUSION

A wide range of chemical and physical properties of poly(acrylic acid) and related water-soluble acrylic polymers has been demonstrated, and this variety has been applied to many, useful applications. Obviously, there is much in the chemistry of these polyelectrolytes that requires further elucidation. As this work is carried out, and as further modifications in copolymer structure are obtained, an increased sphere of applications assuredly will follow.

W. H. Montgomery

Research Department
Cyanamid International
Wayne, New Jersey

9

Polyacrylamide

In 1955 acrylamide monomer became a commercial reality. This new monomer had long been known to produce water-soluble polymers, either through copolymerization with other monomers or through homopolymerization. The availability of acrylamide gave industry an effective means of manufacturing reactive polymers — anionic, cationic, or nonionic in character — to meet the requirements of modern technology.

Important needs of the process and formulation industries have been filled by these polymers, either through the chemical reactivity of the polymers or through polymers with the composition, molecular weight, or degree of cross-linking required for specific applications. For instance, polyacrylamide is now widely used by the process industries for the removal of finely divided solids from aqueous solutions, and the dry strength of paper is improved greatly by adding an anionic acrylamide-acrylic acid copolymer to the pulp.

These polymers and copolymers are now produced in large quantities and have far greater uniformity than natural water-soluble gums.

MANUFACTURE OF POLYACRYLAMIDE

The steps in the manufacture of acrylamide are given in the simplified reaction scheme shown on the following page.

Purified acrylamide is a white crystalline solid having a molecular weight of 71.08 and a melting point of 84 to 85C. It is soluble in water, butyl Cellosolve,* dioxane, ethyl alcohol, methyl alcohol, and ethyl acetate; but only slightly soluble in hydrocarbon solvents.

Acrylamide may be polymerized and copolymerized by a variety of techniques including solution polymerization by means of catalysts, light-sensitive dyes, or ultrasonic waves. Crystalline acrylamide will polymerize

* Registered trademark of Union Carbide Corporation.

175

when irradiated with gamma rays. Graft and block polymers of acrylamide also can be prepared.

$$C_3H_6 + NH_3 + O_2 \xrightarrow[\text{300-400C}]{\substack{\text{Catalyst} \\ \text{(Bi, P, Mo, etc. salts)}}}$$

$$\underset{\textit{Acrylonitrile}}{CH_2=CHCN} \xrightarrow[\text{H}_2\text{SO}_4]{\text{H}_2\text{O}} \underset{\textit{Acrylamide}}{CH_2=CH-\overset{\displaystyle O}{\overset{\|}{C}}-NH_2}$$

Acrylamide has been copolymerized with a large variety of monomers. In general, the degree of water solubility of the copolymer is a function of the acrylamide content of the copolymer. A few of the monomers with which acrylamide has been copolymerized are: acrolein, acrylates, acrylic acid, acrylonitrile, butadiene, butyl methacrylate, diallyl cyanamide, glycidyl acrylate, maleic anhydride, methacrylamide, methacrylic acid, methyl acrylate, styrene, unsaturated acyl gelatins, unsaturated alkyds, vinyl acetate, vinyl chloride, vinyl ethers and ketones, vinylpyridines, and N-vinylpyrrolidone.

Polymers produced through the homopolymerization of acrylamide are essentially nonionic (although some carboxyl function may develop through hydrolysis during manufacture), while the copolymers of acrylamide and acidic monomers are anionic.

Commercial processes for preparing polyacrylamide have been developed which give precise control of the properties of the polymers. In many cases the same plant facilities are used for the manufacture of a wide variety of polymers and copolymers.

PROPERTIES OF ACRYLAMIDE POLYMERS

Polyacrylamide is readily soluble in cold water. Heating does not significantly increase the rate of solution. Care must be exercised to add the polymer in small portions to the vortex of the liquid at such a rate that there is immediate dispersion of the solids. To insure good dispersion, the rate of addition of the polymer must be reduced as the viscosity of the solution increases. Certain manufacturers of acrylamide polymers recommend a simple dispersion apparatus. Like other water-soluble products, poor dispersion leads to the formation of "fish eyes."

As a means of obtaining good dispersion, some of the commercially available polyacrylamides are in flake or granular form. In applications where small quantities of an alcohol can be tolerated, polyacrylamide may be dispersed in a water-soluble alcohol and the mixture added to water with agitation.

The solubility of polyacrylamide in organic compounds is generally very limited. Several compounds have sufficient solvent effect to act as plasticizers; for example, ethylene glycol, glycerol, dioxolane, anhydrous glycolonitrile, lactonitrile, morpholine, propylene glycol, and alcohol-ethylene oxide adducts.

The viscosity of an aqueous solution containing a given quantity of polyacrylamide is a function of the molecular weight of the polymer. For the most part, the range of molecular weights of the commercial polyacrylamides is 30,000 to 12,000,000. The Brookfield viscosity-concentration relationship for solutions of polyacrylamide with a molecular weight of 3,000,000 to 5,000,000 is shown in Figure 9.1. The change in Brookfield viscosity with

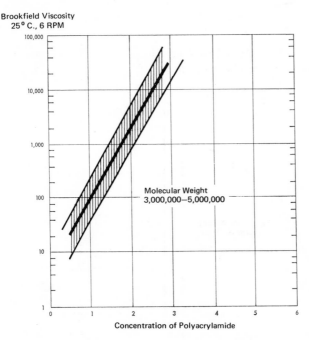

FIGURE 9.1 Viscosity (Brookfield)-concentration relationship for polyacrylamide solutions.

temperature for aqueous solutions of a typical polyacrylamide is shown in Figure 9.2.

Aqueous solutions of polyacrylamide are non-Newtonian liquids exhibit-

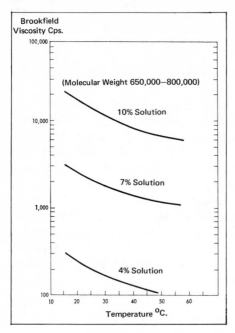

FIGURE 9.2 Viscosity (Brookfield) change with temperature for aqueous polyacrylamide solutions.

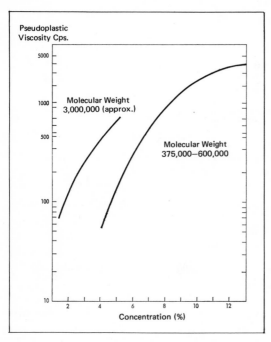

FIGURE 9.3 Pseudoplastic viscosities for polyacrylamide solutions at 30C using Green viscosimeter.

ing pseudoplastic flow under conditions of shear. This is evident from Figure 9.3, which shows the relationship of viscosity to concentration for two typical polyacrylamides.

Because of the nonionic nature of polyacrylamide, the change in solution viscosity with changes in pH is not great between pH 1 and 10. When stored at pH levels above 10, however, the polymer is subject to hydrolysis and rapid increase in viscosity. Figure 9.4 shows the general effect of changes in

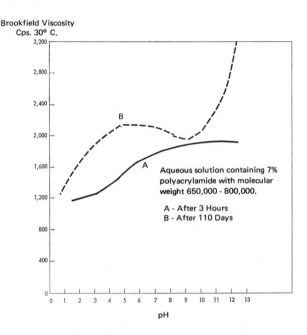

FIGURE 9.4 Viscosity (Brookfield)-pH relationship for polyacrylamide solutions.

pH on the viscosities of solutions of polyacrylamide which have aged for different periods of time.

Solutions of polyacrylamide have excellent tolerance for electrolytes such as ammonium chloride, calcium sulfate, cupric sulfate, potassium hydroxide, sodium bicarbonate, sodium borate, sodium nitrate, sodium phosphates (mono-, di-, and tri-basic), sodium sulfate, zinc chloride, boric acid, phosphoric acid, and sulfuric acid. Surface-active agents also are compatible with solutions of polyacrylamide as well as styrene-butadiene, polyvinyl acetate, polyacrylate latexes, and emulsified alkyds.

An aqueous solution of polyacrylamides is not subject to attack by microorganisms but will provide a substrate for the growth of mold if nutrients are present. Hence when solutions of polyacrylamide are placed in storage, they should contain a suitable biocide.

REACTIONS

The reactivity of the amide groups in polyacrylamide gives the polymer a broad field of application. In many cases the polymer is reacted *in situ* with other components of a formulation. On the other hand, ionic derivatives of polyacrylamide may be prepared. Schiller and Suen prepared such a group of polymers and evaluated them in paper treatment, soil conditioning, drilling muds, and in settling sewage.

Polyacrylamide may be converted to a polymer containing carboxylate groups through the hydrolysis of its amide groups. This reaction occurs under alkaline conditions. The hydrolysis is easily controlled to give a polymer having the sodium carboxylate content needed for a specific application.

When the required carboxyl content (expressed as acrylic acid) is less than 20 per cent, copolymerization of acrylamide and acrylic acid is the preferred route. Hydrolyzed polyacrylamides and acrylamide-acrylic acid copolymers are easily insolubilized by the addition of alum or some other trivalent salt.

Polyacrylamide reacts with formaldehyde to give methylolated polyacrylamide which can be made insoluble by the addition of an acid or by drying at 100C. The reaction with formaldehyde is carried out under alkaline conditions at room temperature. Since this is an equilibrium reaction, some free formaldehyde remains. The product from this reaction must be stored at pH levels of 7 to 10 to prevent gelling.

The nonionic character of polyacrylamide can be changed through reactions involving the amide groups. An anionic derivative is obtained from the sulfomethylolation of the polymer with formaldehyde and sodium bisulfite at pH levels of 10 to 12. The product has been shown to be comparable to some of the commercial products used in drilling muds and soil conditioning.

A cationic polyacrylamide, effective in imparting wet strength to paper when added to alkaline stock, is a product made through the reaction of polyacrylamide with alkaline hydrochlorite. Another cationic derivative, prepared by reacting polyacrylamide with an amine and formaldehyde, increases the rate of settling sewage by a factor of 4.

In many applications it is necessary to have a water-soluble polymer which has reasonable solubility in alcohols. This type of polymer is obtained when ethylene oxide is reacted with polyacrylamide at a molar ratio of at least 14 to 1.

Insolubilization

The reactivity of polyacrylamide provides several ways to insolubilize the polymer. Most of the following procedures produce a water-insoluble polymer if the polyacrylamide has a high molecular weight. The insoluble polymer may swell when exposed to conditions of high humidity.

(1) Add 0.1 to 0.6 per cent Accobond* 3900 Bonding Agent (based on the polyacrylamide in the formulation) and an acid salt such as ammonium acetate, ammonium acid phosphate, calcium chloride, or magnesium chloride to pH 4 to 6 and dry at room temperature. This form of polyacrylamide remains insoluble below pH of 7.

(2) Heat polyacrylamide with sodium hydroxide for two hours at 90C and add a trivalent salt.

(3) React polyacrylamide with glyoxal under alkaline conditions.

(4) React polyacrylamide with formaldehyde at pH 10 to 10.5 and treat with an acid or free radical or heat the reaction product (adjusted to pH 7 to 8) to 100C.

(5) Boil polyacrylamide with acetic anhydride for 10 to 15 minutes and cure at 150C for 10 to 15 minutes.

(6) When a solution, containing 3 per cent polyacrylamide and having a molecular weight of approximately six million, is made with 0.4 per cent $CrCl_3 \cdot 6H_2O$ and is acidified and dried, the resulting film is 99 per cent insoluble. The starting formulation is stable for at least three months.

Plasticizers

Polyacrylamide in its soluble or insoluble forms produces hard, brittle films. In some cases it is desirable to incorporate about 5 per cent of a plasticizer in formulations containing polyacrylamide to obtain improved flexibility. Such plasticizers include: Polyglycol P400** (polypropylene glycol), Renex*** 30 (tridecyl alcohol-ethylene oxide adduct), and Tween**** 80 (sorbitan monooleate-ethylene oxide adduct).

INDUSTRIAL USES OF POLYACRYLAMIDE

Mining and Process Industries

In the beneficiation of minerals and in the process industries solids must be separated from the water, or from the process streams in which they are

* Registered trademark of American Cyanamid Company.
** Registered trademark of Dow Chemical Company.
*** Registered trademarks of Atlas Powder Company.
**** Registered trademarks of American Cyanamid Company.

suspended. The separation process can either be setting, filtration, centrifuging, or combinations thereof. The objective of the separation is either the recovery of a valuable relatively water-free cake or of a valuable filtrate, or the production of solid and liquid products suitable for disposal.

When a high molecular weight polyacrylamide flocculant is added to a suspension of fine solids, the colloidal particles in the suspension are tied together to form heavy agglomerates known as "flocs" that form in a random manner and settle rapidly, leaving a supernatant liquor free of solids. The amount of flocculant required is low, usually about 0.01 to 0.1 lb/ton of solids in suspension, added as a very dilute solution, often 0.01 per cent solids by weight. Figures 9.5 and 9.6 show the effect on settling rate obtained through the addition of polyacrylamide flocculants to slurries of bituminous coal and to dispersions of acid-washed silica.

Increased dosages of flocculant solution will produce increases in the

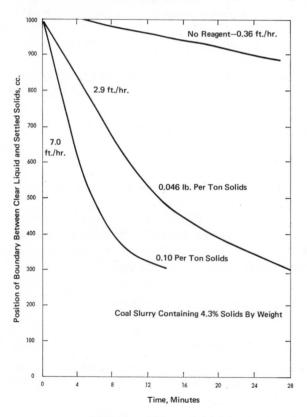

FIGURE 9.5 Effect of high molecular weight polyacrylamide on bituminous coal slurry.

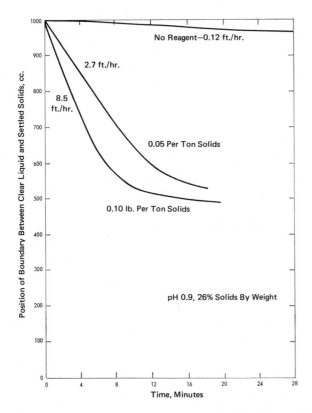

FIGURE 9.6   Effect of high molecular weight polyacrylamide on acid-leached uranium ore.

settling rate. However, there can be an optimum concentration of flocculant above which settling rates actually are reduced (see Figure 9.7), because most of the surfaces of the individual particles are covered with polymer and there are very few sites onto which new ties between particles can form. Excessive agitation can also reduce settling efficiency by breaking the ties between the particles causing the freshly formed surfaces to be covered with polymer and preventing the formation of larger flocs.

The efficiency of the flocculant is often improved by stage addition of the flocculant solution along a pipe or launder carrying the suspension. The use of an inorganic electrolyte such as alum or lime in a flocculant solution can at times further increase setting rate or overflow clarity.

If a flocculant is not present in settling operations, only the heavier solid particles drop to the bottom of the settling chamber in a reasonable length of time while finely divided solids remain suspended in the supernatant

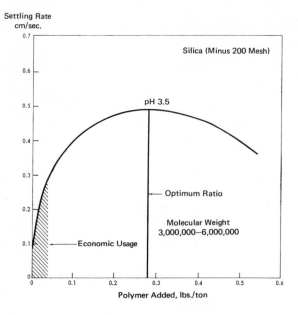

FIGURE 9.7 Effect of high molecular weight polyacrylamide on settling rate of 200-mesh silica.

liquor. In an undisturbed system, these fines may stay suspended for days. They will, however, be settled very rapidly through the use of acrylamide polymers.

In filtration, the addition of a polyacrylamide flocculant to the feed will improve filtration rates markedly and the filter cake is usually firmer and at times drier. Washability of the cake is improved, blinding of the filter is reduced, and discharge of the cake is facilitated. Where a settling operation is followed by a filtration operation, the use of a polymer in the settling operation will also aid the subsequent filtration step.

In centrifuging, it is difficult to make a good solid-liquid separation, particularly when suspensions are treated that contain a large proportion of colloidal or near-colloidal particles. The addition of a very high molecular weight polymer will produce flocs tough enough to withstand the mechanical action of the centrifuge and thus enable the production of a clear overflow.

In leaching vessels, solid particles will settle out of the suspension when the agitators are stopped, thus plugging the outlets of the tanks and blocking the agitator blades. The addition of polyacrylamide flocculants will integrate the finer particles with the coarser particles, and thus form flocs that are easy to clean. In hydrometallurgical operations the addition of polymers to the suspensions provides the further benefit of reducing or even preventing the deposition of insoluble salts in pipelines and filter media.

Paper Industry

The use of polymers and copolymers of acrylamide in the paper industry has resulted in greater operating efficiencies. The development of these products is largely based on an understanding of the relationship of the carboxyl content and the molecular weight of the polymer to the function of the polymer in the paper-making process. This relationship is shown in Figure 9.8.

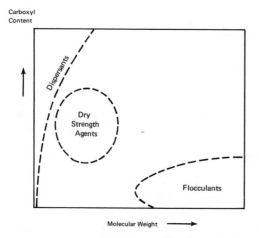

FIGURE 9.8 Application of polyacrylamides in the paper industry.

The paper industry has many problems involving flocculation. High molecular weight acrylamide polymers, when used in quantities of 0.1 to 1.0 lb/ton of fiber, give improved filler retention and better dewatering of the stock, resulting in significant reduction in clay and pigment usage. Polymers and copolymers of acrylamide also provide improved sizing from rosin sizes, faster drainage, wet web strength, and lower steam consumption in the dryer. Polyacrylamide is being used in white water clarification.

In addition to improved operating efficiencies in the paper-making, process, increased dry strength of the sheet with very little increase in the wet strength is obtained through the use of acrylamide-acrylic copolymers with low concentrations of alum present in pulp suspensions. Figure 9.9 shows the relationship of dry tensile strength to the concentration of alum in a bleached sulphite–hardwood kraft–pulp blend with this copolymer, and, in contrast, without the copolymer. Highly refined pulp gives a sheet with much higher dry strength when the copolymer is used, as shown in Figure 9.10.

The addition of a water-soluble cationic nonthermosetting resin broadens the effective pH of the copolymer-alum system as indicated in Figure 9.11.

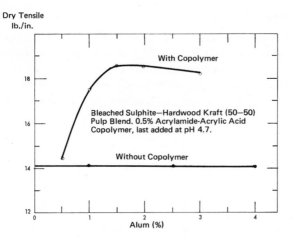

FIGURE 9.9 The effect of changes in alum concentration on the dry tensile of a pulp containing an acrylamide-acrylic acid copolymer.

Oil Well Applications

Polyacrylamides are used in crude oil production to improve the efficiencies of aqueous hydraulic fracturing and waterflood treatment of reservoirs.

In hydraulic fracturing, large volumes of water are pumped through relatively small diameter pipes at high pressures and velocities. Without the use of chemical additives, extremely high pressure drops develop which significantly reduce the pressure available at the formation to create the artificial fracture. Polyacrylamides have proved to be excellent additives because of the compatibility of the polymers with the dissolved salts nearly always present in the water available at the site. Very small quantities of the polymer are required to reduce the friction loss of the fracturing fluid and horsepower requirements of the pumping units. Figure 9.12 compares the pressure drop of pure water with that of water containing polyacrylamide at several concentrations of polymer and at several flow rates.

In the secondary recovery of oil from reservoirs, the oil remaining in the formation is displaced by means of water pumped into injection wells arranged symmetrically around a producing well. In recent years, pilot tests have been conducted in which an extremely dilute aqueous solution of polymer is used at the start of a waterflood, followed by the injection of water containing no polymer for the remainder of the operation. This technique results in a lower ratio of water to oil and in greater efficiency of the waterflood. A possible reason for this improved efficiency is that the aqueous solution of polyacrylamide moves through the formation with a smooth ad-

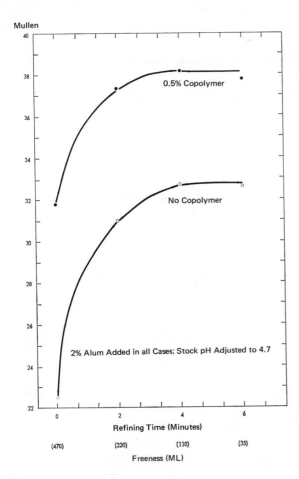

FIGURE 9.10   The effect of acrylamide-acrylic acid copolymer on dry tensile of refined pulp.

vancing front rather than as advancing fingers of unknown and unpredictable lengths.

Water and Waste Water Treatment

In the treatment of water and waste water with flocculants to remove solid matter, the charge on the suspended solids influences the selection of flocculant. High molecular weight nonionic polyacrylamides, often in combination with inexpensive inorganic salts such as alum, are highly efficient in the clarification of ground water. Anionic polymers of acrylamide are

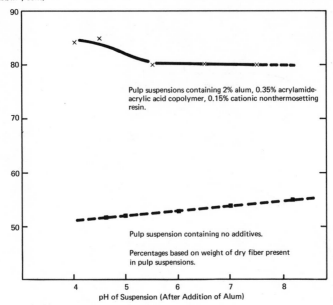

Dry Strength
Mullen
(Lbs/In^2, Corr.)

Pulp suspensions containing 2% alum, 0.35% acrylamide-acrylic acid copolymer, 0.15% cationic nonthermosetting resin.

Pulp suspension containing no additives.

Percentages based on weight of dry fiber present in pulp suspensions.

pH of Suspension (After Addition of Alum)

FIGURE 9.11   The effect of pH on tensile strength of sheet made from stock treated with alum-copolymer-nonthermosetting resin additive system.

often used to flocculate industrial wastes carrying a small negative charge. There are, however, many cases in which the nature of the suspended solids requires that a combination of flocculants be used.

OTHER APPLICATIONS OF POLYACRYLAMIDE

There are numerous formulations containing polyacrylamide mentioned in the literature. Following is a representative group which indicates the variety of uses in which polyacrylamide may be employed.

In emulsion polymerization, polyacrylamide acts as a protective colloid to impart freeze-thaw stability to the latex. The following recipe illustrates the use of polyacrylamide as a protective colloid:

	Parts
Vinyl acetate	200
Ammonium persulfate (in 50 parts of water)	1.46
Potassium metabisulfite (in 50 parts of water)	0.72
Aerosol* OT surface-active agent (25%)	5
Sodium bicarbonate (6.6% in water)	15
Polyacrylamide (10% in water)	135

* Registered trademark of American Cyanamid Company.

188

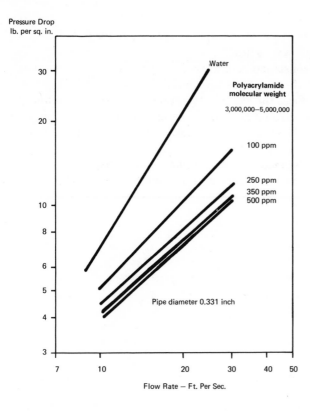

FIGURE 9.12   The effect of addition of high molecular weight poly-acrylamide on pressure drop.

Aerosol OT, sodium bicarbonate, and the polyacrylamide are heated to 80C. Some (15 per cent) of the monomer is added slowly, followed by 15 parts of each catalyst solution. The mixture is refluxed and after 30 minutes most of the monomer is polymerized. The balance of the monomer is added over a 60-minute period and 5 parts of each catalyst solution are added when each one-seventh of the monomer has been added. During the monomer-catalyst addition, the temperature is held at $80 \pm 2C$. After the addition of the monomer-catalyst solution is complete, the batch is held at 85C for one hour and then cooled.

Regenerated cellulose fibers are given dimensional stability by adding about 3 per cent polyacrylamide to the dope just before it is pumped through the spinnerets. After the rayon-polyacrylamide fiber has been processed, it is rendered insoluble through reaction with formaldehyde. This is another example of the use of the reactive nature of polyacrylamide to obtain compositions having unique properties.

In the building and construction industry, a polyacrylamide-type product reduces the water loss of cement grouts. The addition of 0.7 to 1.5 per cent polymer effectively reduces the loss of water from a portland cement grout.

Polyacrylamide in electro-refining processes is the subject of a patent in which greater current efficiencies and a smooth, dense, and uniform deposit of metal are claimed.

An interesting development in the baking enamel field is a series of copolymers of acrylamide and other vinyl monomers.

R. H. Harding
J. K. Rose

Technical Center
Union Carbide Corporation
South Charleston, West Virginia

10

Ethylene Oxide Polymers

The history of very high molecular weight ethylene oxide polymers in this country began in the early 1950's with fundamental studies on the reactions of alkylene oxides.

Today, very high molecular weight polymers of ethylene oxide, called Polyox water-soluble resins, are produced by Union Carbide.

These resins are granular, nonionic poly(ethylene oxide) homopolymers ranging in molecular weight from several hundred thousand to five million and above. They differ from other polyalkylene oxide analogs in being truly thermoplastic and completely soluble in water. Films of these resins are inherently flexible, tough, and resistant to most oils and greases.

They are compatible with many organic solvents, detergent compositions, and with moderate concentrations of electrolytes, as well as many synthetic and natural polymers. Disposal of the resin in waste streams is no problem, because the resins are completely water-soluble and undergo biological decomposition very slowly.

The properties of poly(ethylene oxide) in water solution are of special interest in the investigation of colloidal systems where a polymer possessing extraordinary thickening power is desired or where a nonionic flocculant is needed.

Being thermoplastic, the resin is readily calendered, extruded, molded or cast. Sheets and films of this material are heat-sealable. The polymer crystallites tend to orient in the direction of stretch, and consequently, the films can develop a high degree of strength.

The polymer is largely linear, with sufficient mobility under most conditions to form large crystalline aggregates. The high-tensile strengths attained by the oriented polymer, and the sharpness of its melting point, result from its very high degree of crystallinity in the solid state, as high as 95 per cent.

Being polyethers, these resins hydrogen bond strongly with water. This fact accounts for their solvation by water as well as the unusual thickening power of high molecular weight poly(ethylene oxide), the inverse solubility-temperature relationship, and the high degree of pseudoplasticity of these solutions.

Polyox resin undergoes the normal salting-out effects associated with neutral molecules in solution and high dielectric media. The result is to depress the upper temperature limit of solubility, and reduce the viscosity of both dilute and concentrated solutions of the polymers.

Poly(ethylene oxide) resins are produced in a number of grades. Polyox, for instance, is made in the eight grades shown in Table 10.1. The four WSR resins have high thickening power in aqueous media. The four WSR N resins show less pituitousness and produce low solution viscosities at high resin

TABLE 10.1.   Viscosity Grades of Polyox Water-Soluble Resins.

Grade	Approximate Molecular Weight	Viscosity Range (cps) (25C)	
		5% solution	1% solution
Polyox WSR N-10	100,000	10–20	—
Polyox WSR N-80	200,000	55–95	—
Polyox WSR N-750	300,000	550–900	—
Polyox WSR N-3000	600,000	2250–3350	—
Polyox WSR-35	200,000	520–900	—
Polyox WSR-205	600,000	4100–8000	—
Polyox WSR-301	4,000,000	—	1500–3500
Polyox Coagulant	>5,000,000	—	>4000

Polyox is a registered trademark of Union Carbide Corporation.

concentrations. These resins are similar in chemical structure and physical properties, but differ in molecular weight, molecular weight distribution, solution rheology, and plastic properties in the solid state. Physical property data for a typical sample of Polyox are shown in Table 10.2.

Strong association complexes are formed between poly(ethylene oxides)

TABLE 10.2.   Typical Properties of Polyox Water-Soluble Resins.

Melting point	65 ± 2C
Specific gravity	1.21 g/cu cm
Bulk density	17 to 33 lb/cu ft
Moisture content, as supplied	<1%
Ash content, as CaO	0.3 to 0.8%
Heat of fusion	33 cal/g
Particle size	98% through 10 mesh

and a wide variety of materials such as phenols, phenolic resins, mineral acids, halogens, urea, gelatin, asphalts, lignin sulfonic acids, mercuric salts, iodides, and polymeric acids. The latter category includes carboxyl derivatives of cellulose, silicones, and many natural and synthetic organic polymers and copolymers. These association complexes often exhibit properties markedly different from either component alone.

The Polyox resin can associate with various compounds in bulk or solution. Powder mixtures can be compounded on conventional equipment to produce these complexes. Complex formation can be regulated by changes in solution pH, temperature, molecular weight, or by the use of certain organic inhibitors.

A typical example of a poly(ethylene oxide) resin complex is its association with poly(acrylic acid). When aqueous solutions of the two resins are mixed, a heavy white precipitate forms immediately. The crystal structure, heat stability, and elastic behavior of this precipitate are completely different from those of either base material. While poly(acrylic acid) is essentially amorphous and poly(ethylene oxide) resins have crystalline melting points near 65C, the product's crystalline phase melts above 250C. Glass transition temperature and room temperature stiffness vary greatly with the ratio of reactants and cover a range far exceeding those of the individual resins. Additional facts on these complexes are given by K. L. Smith, A. E. Winslow, and D. E. Peterson in *Industrial and Engineering Chemistry*, **51**, No. 11, November 1959, pp. 1361–1364.

Polyox resin complexes with other materials are as follows:

- *Phenolics.* Water-insoluble association products toughen phenolic resins.
- *Mineral Acids.* Complexes gel aqueous solutions.
- *Halogens.* Complexes possess germicidal activity.
- *Ureas.* Water-soluble thermoplastic complex can be calendered, molded, or extruded into tablets and other shapes.
- *Lignin Sulfonic Acids.* Complexes possess good adhesive characteristics.
- *Potassium Iodide.* Complex has low crystallinity and good film clarity.
- *Other Polycarboxylic Compounds.* Complex properties approach those expected from copolymerization.

APPLICATIONS

Poly(ethylene oxide) resins are of interest to manufacturers because of their complete water solubility, high thickening efficiency, high resistance to biological attack, low atmospheric moisture pick-up in dry form, and the soft, silky feel of resin solutions. Also their films are tough and flexible and resist most oils and greases.

Adhesives   Association products of Polyox resins, especially with lignin sulfonic acids, are used as low-cost adhesives for a number of products, including paper, pencils, rubber, shoes, and urethanes as well as in buffing compounds, and as protective strips in paint-masking operations.

Agriculture   Film-forming properties, and their compatibility with a wide range of products, make these resins useful for protective root coatings, for seed coatings and spacings, in soil conditioning and stabilizing, and in water-soluble packaging film.

Aviation   Thickening and stabilizing de-icing fluids.

Building materials   Size and stabilize plaster compositions.

Ceramics   Burn off cleanly at low temperatures, leave no objectionable residues when ceramics are fired; binders, dispersants, stabilizers for pigments.

Cigarettes and cigars   Binders in tobacco sheet manufacture, cigarette filters.

Cosmetics   Complete water-solubility, thickening efficiency, and the soft, silky feel imparted to cosmetic compositions are among the properties that make these resins outstanding as components of numerous creams, lotions, shampoos, and powders. They are used in aerosol hair sprays, anti-perspirant creams, cold wave lotions, compressed face powders, contour lotions, cosmetic sticks (anti-perspirant, cake mascara, pancake makeup), face creams, hand creams, pigmented foundation lotions, protective hand lotions, shampoos and shaving preparations.

Glass fibers   Binders and sizes.

Hydraulic fluids   Water-soluble lubricant additives.

Ink   Protective colloids for lithographic inks; water-soluble packaging of oleo-resinous inks and color concentrates.

Metals   Aerosol anti-tarnish coating, electroplating bath additive, investment casting, solder fluxes, welding rod coatings, mold release agent.

Oil   With certain pitches and asphalt emulsions to improve adhesion to substrate or aggregate.

Ore   Sprayed on ore deposits to prevent wind erosion.

Paints   Soluble in methylene chloride for use in paint remover formulations; as paint thickeners in latex systems to achieve a multicolored lacquer effect; water-soluble packaging.

Pharmaceutical   Their high degree of flexibility and strength, their excellence as film formers, and their soft, silky feel when incorporated in lotions, coatings, and pastes make Polyox resins well suited for pharmaceutical applications. Applications include aerosol applied plastic bandages, calamine lotions, dental adhesives, tablet binders and coatings, and toothpaste.

Photography In photographic gel systems to increase both the tensile strength and extensibility of gelatin films.

Resins As plasticizers for poly(vinyl acetate) resins, glue, gelatin, and many naturally occurring materials.

Rubber Form stabilizers and as mold release agents for rubber.

Specialties Emulsion formulations containing these resins are used as polishes and waxes for floors and furniture. The excellent lubricity and feel they impart to detergents makes them outstanding for use in detergent bars, liquids, and powders. They are also used in soap powders and as water-soluble packaging for bleaching and bluing powders.

Textiles In binders for nonwoven fabrics; for rug backing and as a textile warp size; as a solubilizer for starch.

Urethanes Foam stabilizers and mold-release agents for urethanes.

GENERAL PROPERTIES

Moisture Sorption

Polyox is relatively resistant to sorption of atmospheric moisture at all but the highest relative humidities (see Figure 10.1).

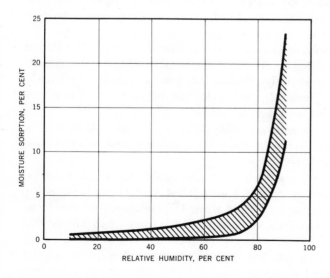

FIGURE 10.1 Moisture sorption of Polyox at various humidities.

Toxicological Properties

These resins have low oral toxicity. Inclusion in the diet of rats at a concentration of 2 per cent for 2 years caused no harm detectable by gross observation. They are non-irritating to the skin and have a low sensitizing potential. The potential for eye injury is also slight. Flooding rabbits' eyes with an aqueous 5 per cent resin solution caused only moderate inflammation of the eye.

Solubility

The solubility of Polyox resins in various solvents is shown in Table 10.3. These resins are miscible with water in all proportions and are soluble in some organic solvents. Small quantities of water markedly increased their solubility in other solvents.

Stability

The molecular weights of solid or molten Polyox and its solutions, may be reduced by oxidation or by mechanical attrition under high shear. Any decrease in molecular weight is accompanied by losses in melt or solution viscosity.

Though all ethers can form peroxides, they never reach explosive proportions in high molecular weight polyethers. They can, however, reduce their degree of polymerization through chain scission. Heat, light, and transition metal ions tend to increase the rate of oxidative attack and should be avoided when possible.

Antioxidants, alcohols, and amines that are effective stabilizers for Polyox resins include: 1-acetyl-2-thiourea, Agerite resin (R. T. Vanderbilt), Agerite White (R. T. Vanderbilt), allyl alcohol, Aminox (Naugatuck Chemical), Aranox (Naugatuck Chemical), diphenylamine, ethanol, ethylene glycol, isopropanol, phenothiazine, thiourea, and uric acid.

These antioxidants are generally effective at 0.5 per cent. Most may be added to the solution or to the dry resin. Isopropanol and the other alcohols are particularly useful in solutions.

Polyox resins can be degraded by ultraviolet light. Molded or extruded articles can be stabilized by the well-known UV stabilizers (e.g. salicylates). An enhanced stabilizing effect results when UV stabilizers are combined with an antioxidant. An effective concentration is from 0.1 to 0.5 per cent each.

In the molten state or in solution, the resin undergoes chain rupture under high shear. The amount of change increases with total energy input and with resin molecular weight.

SOLUTION PREPARATION

Individual resin particles must be thoroughly dispersed during the first 2 or 3 minutes of the dissolving operation. If not, the polymer surfaces adsorb solvent and cohere almost immediately. Prolonged agitation is then needed to dissolve the resulting agglomerate. But by keeping the particles separated for a minute or two, the condition becomes self-correcting.

Mechanical dispersion is possible by using a relatively large diameter, medium speed agitator. Operating in a vessel equipped with well-placed baffles, gives the uniform, turbulent, but not violent agitation needed for good dispersion when used with a special dry resin feeding unit developed for Polyox.

Should a non-solvent method of dispersion be preferred, there are two choices. The boiling water technique is adaptable to small and medium size dissolving operations, where minimal agitation equipment is available. Use is made of the fact that Polyox is insoluble in boiling water, but soluble at all temperatures below this point. The resin is sifted into boiling water (about ⅔ of the total water to be used) and mildly agitated until dispersion is complete. The remainder of the water is added at room temperature with continued agitation, after which the source of heat can be removed.

Another method involves dispersing the resin in a concentrated solution of salts and alkalis, or in water-miscible organic liquids, in which the resin itself is insoluble (see Table 10.3). The dispersions can be stored indefinitely and used as needed. When added to water, the dispersions give solutions quickly and with minimum agitation.

This method is useful for either large or small operations where agitation facilities are limited, and where the dispersing medium is not objectionable. The method gives very rapid solution rates and produces stabilized solutions where isopropanol, ethanol, or ethylene glycol are used as dispersants. The natural tendency for these resin suspensions to settle can be prevented readily by adding small amounts of thickeners if necessary.

The viscosity level of the solution being prepared has a considerable effect upon the solution rate. It is feasible to prepare solutions having viscosities of several hundred thousand centipoises, or even nonflowing gels; like all high viscosity preparations, however, they require considerable time to prepare.

Inverse Solubility

Although poly(ethylene oxide) resins are completely soluble in water at room temperature, they precipitate from water solution at or near the boiling point. Figure 10.2 shows the maximum solution temperature as a function of polymer concentration for a typical Polyox resin.

TABLE 10.3. Solubility of Polyox Water-Soluble Resins in Selected Solvents.
(Solution concentration approximately one per cent by weight)

Solvents	Temperature at which Polyox Resin Precipitates on Cooling, C	Temperature at which Polyox Resin Dissolves on Heating Above 25C
Stay in Solution at 0C		
Water	below 0	—
Acetonitrile	below 0	—
Ethylene dichloride	below 0	—
Carbon tetrachloride	below 0	—
Trichlorethylene	below 0	—
Methylene dichloride	below 0	—
Stay in Solution at Room Temperature		
Benzene	2	—
Isopropanol, 91%	2	—
Dimethylformamide	12	—
Tetrahydrofuran	18	—
Ethylene carbonate	20	—
Methanol	20	—
Methyl ethyl ketone	20	—
Must be Heated to Dissolve		
Toluene	20	30
Xylene	20	30
Acetone	20	35
Cellosolve acetate	25	35
Anisole	0	40
1, 4-Dioxane	4	40
Ethyl acetate	25	40
Ethylene diamine	26	40
Dimethyl Cellosolve	27	40
Cellosolve solvent	28	45
Ethanol, 200 proof	31	45
Carbitol solvent	32	50
Butanol	33	50
Butyl Cellosolve	33	50
Butyl acetate	34	50
Isopropanol, anhydrous	37	50
Methyl isobutyl ketone	40	50
Diethyl Cellosolve	46	50
Insoluble at all Temperatures		
1, 3-Butanediol	—	—
Ethylene glycol	—	—
Diethylene glycol	—	—
Glycerol	—	—

Polyox, Cellosolve, and Carbitol are registered trademarks of Union Carbide Corp.

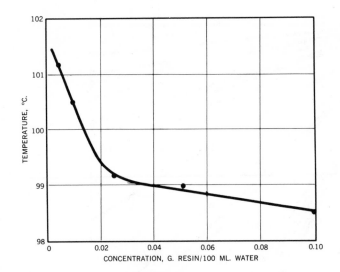

FIGURE 10.2   Upper temperature limit of solubility of poly(ethylene oxide) in water.

The precipitation temperature, observed as a cloud point at low resin concentrations, is very sharp. The polymers precipitate from dilute solutions as particulate floc, and from more concentrated solutions as gels.

Salt Effects

Being nonionic, the resins undergo predictable salting-out effects in water solution. Salts depress the upper temperature limit of solubility and reduce solution viscosities. This salting-out effect is mild in comparison with that observed in the case of polyelectrolytes, but comparable to that observed for other neutral molecules dissolved in high dielectric media.

The effect of concentration of various salts on the solubility temperatures and on intrinsic viscosity are shown in Figures 10.3 and 10.4 respectively.

Table 10.4 compares the relative salting-out power of a number of ions.

Effect of pH

The effect of water solution pH on the upper temperature solubility limit of a typical poly(ethylene oxide) resin is shown in Figure 10.5. Very high hydroxyl ion concentrations reduce precipitation temperature drastically, while very high hydrogen ion concentrations tend to raise it.

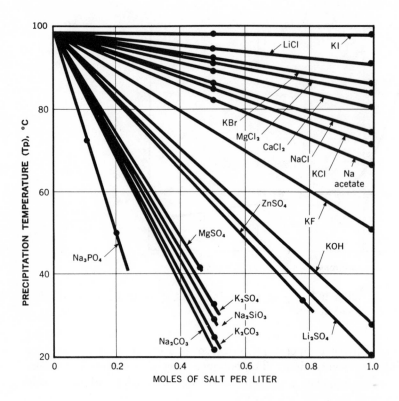

FIGURE 10.3 Upper temperature limit of solubility of poly(ethylene oxide) in salt solutions; resin concentration, 0.5% by weight.

TABLE 10.4. Salting-out Effect of Ions on Poly(Ethylene Oxide).

Decreasing Effectiveness	
Anions	Cations
OH^-	K^+, Na^+
F^-	Li^+
$CO_3^=$, $SO_4^=$	Ca^{++}, Mg^{++}
$CH_3CO_2^-$	Zn^{++}
$CH_2{=}CHCO_2^-$	H^+
Cl^-	
$PO_4^=$	
Br^-, ClO_3^-	

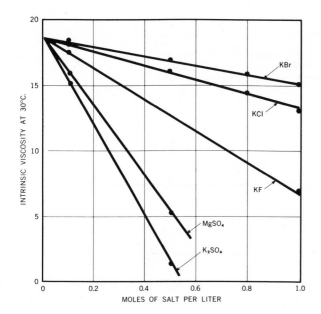

FIGURE 10.4 Intrinsic viscosity of poly(ethylene oxide) in salt solutions.

SOLUTION RHEOLOGY

Pituitousness

Aqueous solutions of poly(ethylene oxide) resins tend to form long strings or filaments when immersed objects are withdrawn. This pituitousness appears to vary exponentially with molecular weight, being quite appreciable in the high molecular weight grades.

Viscosity

Aqueous solutions of high molecular weight resins show considerable structure and an extraordinarily high degree of pseudoplasticity, a reversible reduction of viscosity with increasing shear rate that results from the interaction of these molecules with water. Pseudoplasticity may be apparent in solutions containing only a few hundredths per cent polymer. At 1 to 5 per cent concentrations aqueous solutions of these resins are pituitous as well as pseudoplastic. Solutions more concentrated than about 5 per cent are highly elastic with apparent yield points at low shear rate.

The solution viscosity of Polyox resin appears to vary exponentially with

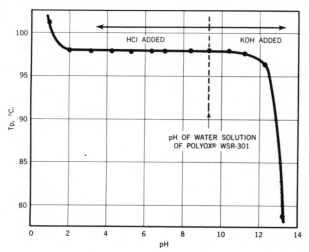

FIGURE 10.5 Upper temperature limit of poly(ethylene oxide) solubility versus the solution pH.

concentration, as illustrated by Figure 10.6. Although equivalent single-point viscosities can be obtained from different molecular-weight grades by adjusting resin concentration, the flow properties of such solutions may be vastly different.

Shear rate is important for poly(ethylene oxide) solutions. For a high polymer solution to flow, the polymer segments must move relative to the solvent. Local viscosity is determined by the solvent as altered by the chain entanglement of the polymer segments. The orientation of solvent (water) along the polymer chain increases the effective volume of the segment which must move with respect to the solvent. Because water itself possesses a hydrogen-bonded polymeric structure, local distortions in the resin chain tend to be stabilized by association with water. This stabilization gives rise to longer relaxation times than would be otherwise predicted, and causes the high shear dependence of the resin solution viscosity, particularly at very low shear rates.

Figure 10.7 illustrates selected effects of shear rate on Polyox resin solution viscosities. The two low molecular weight grades are nearly Newtonian in their flow properties over the usual shear rate ranges. Although not obvious from this figure, pseudoplasticity increases with solution concentration as well as with resin molecular weight.

Increasing temperature reduces the viscosity of resin solutions as illustrated by Figure 10.8. Due to its strong effect, temperature must be strictly controlled when accurate viscosity measurements are required.

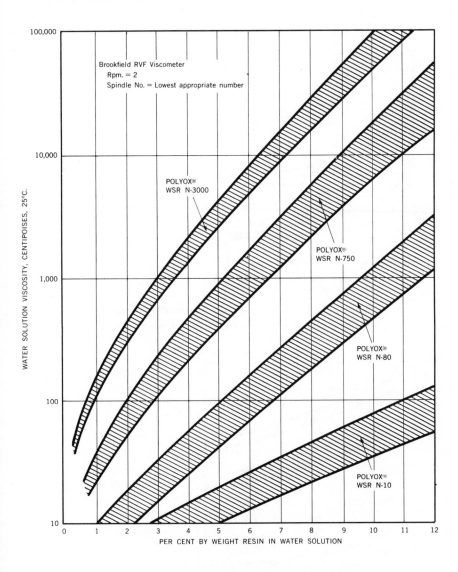

FIGURE 10.6 Viscosity versus concentration of various grades of Polyox in water solutions.

Figure 10.9 shows that pH normally has little effect on the solution viscosity of the resin. The viscosity of a Polyox WSR 301 solution varied less than 3 per cent from pH 2 to pH 12. At a pH below 2, hydrolysis and chain scission may cause a rapid decline in viscosity. At a pH above 12, high

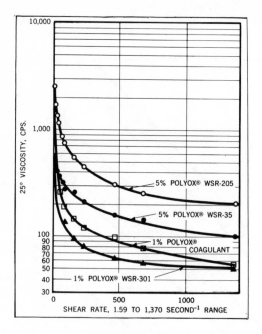

FIGURE 10.7 Viscosity-shear rate relationship for various molecular-weight grades of poly(ethylene oxide) in water solution.

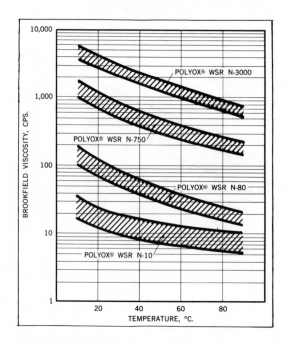

FIGURE 10.8 Viscosity versus temperature for various grades of Polyox in water solution (5.00% by weight).

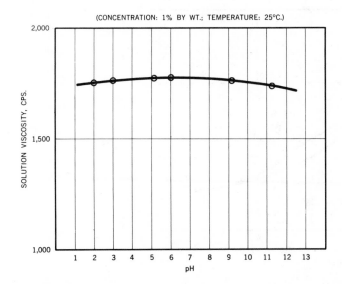

(CONCENTRATION: 1% BY WT.; TEMPERATURE: 25°C.)

FIGURE 10.9 Effect of pH on viscosity of poly(ethylene oxide) water solution.

hydroxyl ion concentration reduces viscosity by precipitating resin from solution.

Electrolytes reduce the dimensions of dissolved polymer molecules, as shown by reductions in their intrinsic viscosities (see Figure 10.4). The ability of salts to reduce the hydrodynamic volume of poly(ethylene oxide) resin molecules parallels their effectiveness in lowering the upper temperature limit of solubility (see Figure 10.3).

Salts exert a marked effect on the viscosity versus shear rate curve. Figure 10.10 compares the flow curves for 2 per cent solutions of a high-molecular-weight poly(ethylene oxide) resin in water and in 0.45 M potassium sulfate (K_2SO_4).

Viscosity Determination

Certain precautions are necessary to measure polymer solution viscosities accurately and reproducibly. The diverse viscometers used in standard industrial tests employ different shear rates, and consequently, give different results for the same solution. If shear rates were truly equivalent, all instruments would indicate the same viscosity value for the same solution. In addition to shear rate, poly(ethylene oxide) resin solution viscosities are sensitive to small variations in temperature and concentration.

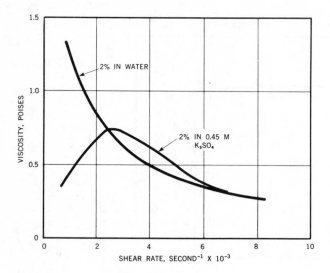

FIGURE 10.10 Viscosity-shear rate relationship for poly(ethylene oxide) as affected by addition of a salt.

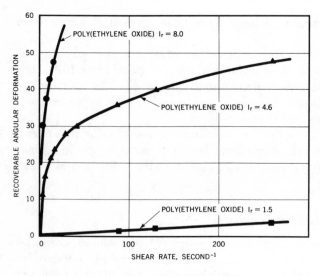

Here, the recoverable angular deformation in degrees, as measured on five per cent by weight solutions of poly(ethylene oxide) with a Haake "Rotovisco", is plotted against shear rate. The sharp increase in angular deformation, and therefore in viscoelasticity, with molecular weight can be noted.

FIGURE 10.11 Effect of molecular weight on viscoelasticity of poly-(ethylene oxide).

In reporting viscosity measurements, the type of viscometer should be specified and the conditions of the test stated in order to convey the data properly.

Molecular Weight Relationships

The molecular weights of Polyox resins have been determined by light scattering and ultracentrifugation techniques for correlation with intrinsic viscosity and sedimentation constants. In water at 30C, and over the molecular weight range of 10^4 to 10^7, the sedimentation constant (S_o) is a classical "Power Law" function of weight average molecular weight (MW):

$$S_o = 1.26 \times 10^{-15} \, MW^{0.41}$$

A similar power law expression derived from light scattering data relates intrinsic viscosity [η] to average molecular weight:

$$[\eta] = 1.25 \times 10^{-4} \, MW^{0.78}$$

In both expressions, molecular weights were calculated from the Flory-Mandelkern relationship.

Viscoelasticity

Solutions of the resin exhibit unusually high levels of viscoelastic behavior. This phenomenon has been attributed to the inherent flexibility of the ether linkage and to the very high molecular weight of the linear molecule. Its response to molecular weight is reflected by Figure 10.11, where recoverable angular deformation and reduced viscosity (I_r) are functions of solution viscoelasticity and resin molecular weight, respectively. Molecular weight distribution can also be expected to affect similar correlations.

Friction Reduction

Very small concentrations of the higher molecular weight Polyox resins can reduce the turbulent frictional drag of the water in which they are dissolved by as much as 80 per cent.

Figure 10.12 relates drag reduction in a cylindrical pipe to resin solution concentration: 30 ppm of Polyox WSR-301 eliminated 66 per cent of water's inherent frictional drag.

The friction-reducing qualities of several typical water-dispersable polymers are compared with poly(ethylene oxide) resin solutions in Figure 10.13. The curves show that the torque required to rotate an immersed disk was reduced more by Polyox resin than by the other commercial polymers.

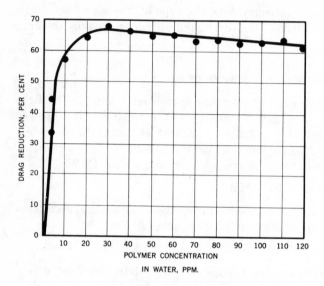

FIGURE 10.12 Friction reduction of typical water-dispersable polymer solutions. Data is for Polyox WSR-301; flow through a 0.109-cm ID pipe at 21.10 and a Reynolds Number of approximately 14,000.

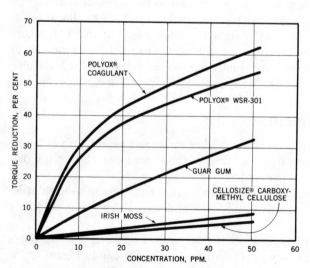

FIGURE 10.13 Comparison of friction-reducing qualities of various water-dispersable polymers.

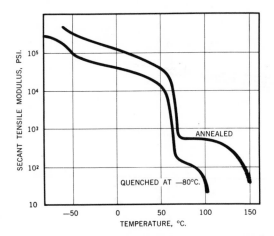

FIGURE 10.14 Stiffness (resistance to plastic flow) of annealed and quenched poly(ethylene oxide) at various temperatures.

PLASTIC PROPERTIES

Poly(ethylene oxide) resin molecules form highly ordered structures at room temperature. Crystallinities of 95 per cent have been estimated for these resins from nuclear magnetic resonance data.

The melting point of Polyox resins changes but slightly over the entire molecular weight range. Despite a sharp loss of crystallinity at the melting point, Figure 10.14 shows that resistance to plastic flow (stiffness) is still very great at higher temperatures.

This very high melt viscosity persists throughout most of the molecular weight range, even when the temperature is raised 150 to 250F (90 to 140C) above the melting point (Figure 10.15).

Because the molten resins are highly pseudoplastic, their viscosities decrease by several orders of magnitude as shear increases from very low to moderately high rates (see Figure 10.16). The dependence of melt viscosity upon shear rate appears to increase slightly with increasing molecular weight of the polymer (see Figure 10.17).

Tensile Properties

The resins are characterized by high extensibility, inherent flexibility, and a tendency to orient under stress. Typical behavior under load is shown in Figures 10.18A and 10.18B where yield strength and breaking strength

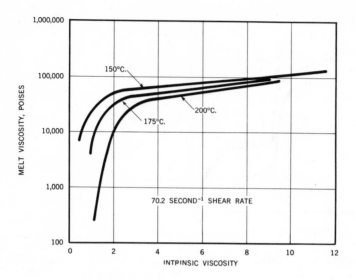

FIGURE 10.15 Effect of temperature on the melt viscosity of poly-(ethylene oxide).

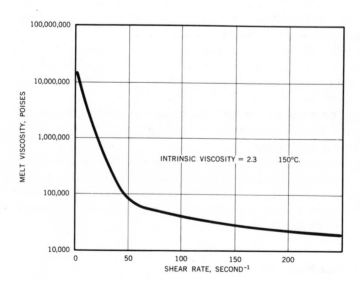

FIGURE 10.16 Variation of poly(ethylene oxide) melt viscosity with shear rate.

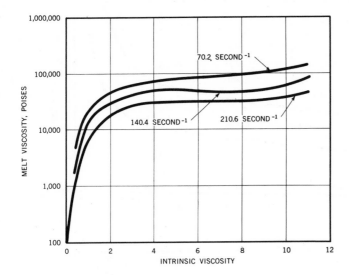

FIGURE 10.17 Effect of poly(ethylene oxide) shear rate on melt viscosity at 150C.

were calculated on the basis of minimum cross-sectional area at the yield and ultimate loads, respectively.

Tensile properties of the resins are not greatly affected by contact with relative humidities below about 70 per cent. At 90 per cent relative humidity, strengths show a significant drop (see Figure 10.19). Tensile modulus (stiffness) drops from about 50,000 psi at normal humidities to about 3000 psi at 90 per cent RH. Polymer extension at the yield point drops slightly at high humidities. Polyox resin tensile behavior under varying conditions follows, in general, the moisture sorption pattern for the material. In other words, relatively low moisture sorption results in substantial immunity to change in most properties up to 70 per cent relative humidity. Upon contact with water, however, there is an almost instantaneous drop in strength, followed rapidly by dissolution.

Water-Soluble Films

Completely water-soluble films may be prepared from poly(ethylene oxide) resins by standard calendering, molding, casting, and extrusion techniques. These films may be clear or opaque. They are inherently flexible, tough, and resistant to most oils and greases. They provide better solubility than other water-soluble plastics without sacrificing strength or toughness.

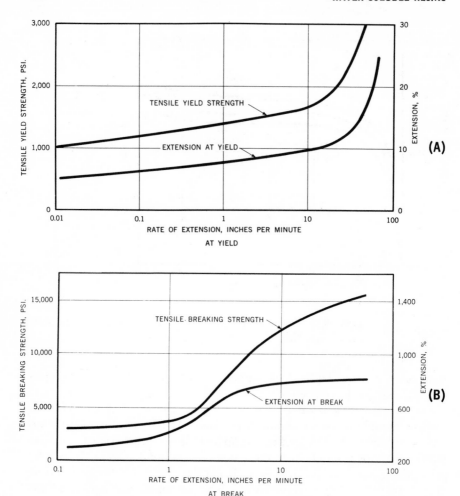

FIGURE 10.18   Tensile behavior of poly(ethylene oxide): (A) Yield data; (B) Break data.

Union Carbide produces two types of clear poly(ethylene oxide) films and sheeting in thicknesses varying from 1.5 to 10 mil (WDAA-4001 and WDAB-4301). These products are marketed under the Radel trademark. Typical physical properties are shown in Table 10.5.

As a heat-sealable thermoplastic, Radel water-soluble film gives strong, leakproof closures at temperatures in the range of 160 to 325F. Strong fusion seals can be achieved with WDAA-4001 film by conventional hot bar, impulse, and radio frequency sealing techniques. Solvent-sealing using water

TABLE 10.5. Typical Properties of Radel poly(Ethylene Oxide) Water-Soluble Films.

Property	Radel Film Grade	
	WDAA-4001	WDAB-4301
Thickness, mil	2.0	2.0
Specific gravity, g/cm^3	1.2	1.2
Area factor, sq in.	11,300	11,300
Tensile strength lb/sq in.		
MD	8,000	8,000
TD	2,000	1,400
Secant modulus at 1%, lb/sq in.		
MD	86,000	33,000
TD	90,000	44,000
Tear strength, g/mil		
MD	10–20	20
TD	No tear	No tear
Dart impact at 50% failure, g	60	225
Shrinkage, % (70C — 10 minutes)		
MD	57.3	60
TD	5.7	8.0
Solubility at 40C		
Release contents, seconds	6.6	8.2
Complete solution, seconds	80	400+
Haze, %	10	13
Specular transmission, %	27	25
Appearance	Clear	Clear
Oxygen transmission, g/100 in.^{2}/24 hr/mil	500	—
Melting point, C	66	66
Heat sealing temperature range, F	160–325	190–225
Cold crack resistance, C	< -70	< -70
Dielectric constant		
60 cycles	3.13	—
10^3 cycles	2.55	—
10^6 cycles	2.19	—
Power factor		
60 cycles	0.50	—
10^3 cycles	0.21	—
10^6 cycles	0.008	—
Dielectric strength	Too low to test	—
Volume resistivity, megohms-cm	2.6×10^3	—
Surface resistivity, megohms	1.99×10^7	—

MD = Machine direction   TD = Transverse direction
Radel is a registered trademark of Union Carbide Corp.

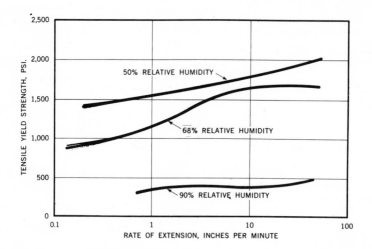

FIGURE 10.19 Effect of relative humidity on yield strength of poly-(ethylene oxide).

or many organics may also be used, but causes cloudiness and is not recommended.

Tight, tough, water-soluble packets for powders to be added to aqueous formulations can be readily produced in a wide range of sizes. These packets are particularly suited to packaging toxic or costly materials. Products such as mercurial powders, fungicides, sanitizing agents, etc. can be packaged in Radel film using standard packaging equipment without difficulty.

The excellent layflat, stiffness, and sealability of Radel water-soluble films make for good machine handling characteristics. Radel WDAA-4001 film can be run on most polyethylene converting equipment. A number of bag-making machines have been run successfully with Radel. Films of Radel WDAB-4301 are softer and more elastic than Radel WDAA-4001, and thus are somewhat more difficult to run on these machines. They still possess acceptable machineability characteristics.

These films can be printed on conventional printing equipment, using either water-soluble or water-insoluble inks. A typical water-soluble ink formulation that has good adhesion to the film without pre-treatment is as follows:

Ingredient	Per Cent
Luxol Fast Red B Dye	14.5
Zein 210	18.1
*Carbowax Polyethylene Glycol 1540	4.8
Water	4.8
Ethyl alcohol	57.8
	100.0

* Carbowax is a registered trademark of Union Carbide Corporation.

Tinting in a wide range of colors is possible by incorporating various color concentrates during processing. Some colors that have been evaluated are:

Color	Color Concentrate	Concentration, Per Cent
Pink	Mercadium Red	0.15
Blue	FD and C Blue No. 1	0.15
Yellow	FD and C Yellow No. 5	0.15

All Radel films have slight reductions of physical strength when exposed to increasing humidity without adequate protection. Typical film property changes for Radel WDAA-4001 film with increasing humidity are shown in the following tabulation. Films were aged 24 hours at each humidity level.

Property	Relative Humidity, Per Cent at 75F		
	30	50	80
Tensile strength, psi			
MD	10,000	12,500	10,300
TD	3,700	2,500	1,100
Elongation, per cent			
MD	210	260	375
TD	650	800	1,150

L. E. Davis

Technical Service and Development
The Dow Chemical Company
Midland, Michigan

11

Polyethylenimine

This chapter describes a relatively new family of polymers, the poly-ethylenimines. Although polyethylenimine has been a chemical curiosity for approximately 80 years and available commercially to researchers for 30 years, its high production cost made commercial application impractical. In June, 1963, The Dow Chemical Company announced an economical process for preparing the parent monomer, ethylenimine which resulted in favorable economics for production of the polymer. The polymer family is now commercially available from Dow as polyethylenimine.

Other suppliers of polyethylenimine include Badische Anilin und Soda-Fabrik A. G. of Germany (Polyamin) and the Chemiad Corporation, New Brunswick, New Jersey.

MANUFACTURING PROCESS

Polyethylenimine is prepared by the polymerization of ethylenimine in the presence of an acid catalyst. The acid acts as a proton donor and the reactive species results in the formation of a "charged ring" followed by a ring cleavage. The charged intermediate can also be formed by employing quaternizing or alkylating agents. The "charged" species reacts with the monomer to initiate the polymerization process:

$$
\begin{array}{c}
\mathrm{CH_2} \\
| \quad \diagdown \\
\quad \quad \mathrm{NH} + \mathrm{H^+ \ or \ R \times} \longrightarrow \left[\begin{array}{cc} \mathrm{CH_2} & \mathrm{H} \\ | \quad \diagup\diagdown & \\ \quad \mathrm{N} & \\ \mathrm{CH_2} & \mathrm{H} \end{array} \right]^+ \ \mathrm{or} \ \left[\begin{array}{cc} \mathrm{CH_2} & \mathrm{R} \\ | \quad \diagup\diagdown & \\ \quad \mathrm{N} & \\ \mathrm{CH_2} & \mathrm{H} \end{array} \right]^+ + \mathrm{X^-} \\
\mathrm{CH_2}
\end{array}
$$

$$
\left[\begin{array}{cc} \mathrm{CH_2} & \mathrm{H} \\ | \quad \diagup\diagdown & \\ \quad \mathrm{N} & \\ \mathrm{CH_2} & \mathrm{H} \end{array} \right]^+ + \begin{array}{c} \mathrm{CH_2} \\ | \quad \diagdown \\ \quad \mathrm{NH} \\ \mathrm{CH_2} \end{array} \longrightarrow \mathrm{H_2NCH_2CH_2N} \begin{array}{c} \mathrm{CH_2} \\ \diagup \ ^{+}\mathrm{H} \\ \diagdown \\ \mathrm{CH_2} \end{array}
$$

The general formula for polyethylenimine is:

$$-(CH_2CH_2NH)_n-$$

However, this formula is misleading because in reality the polymer is highly branched rather than linear. A more typical structure is:

$$H_2N-(CH_2CH_2N)_x-(CH_2CH_2NH)_y-$$

$$CH_2$$

$$CH_2$$

$$-N-$$

The polymer molecule is thought to be elliptical in shape similar to the shape of a football. The resulting polymer has primary, secondary, and tertiary amine nitrogens. Analysis and physical structure has shown that the ratio of primary, to secondary, to tertiary nitrogen in the polymer is approximately $1 : 2 : 1$. These various amine nitrogens provide a polymer which displays unique versatility as a chemical intermediate.

The polymers are currently available in five different molecular weight ranges. The lower molecular weight liquid polymers are available in the anhydrous form, and the higher molecular weights are available as aqueous solutions. Table 11.1 lists polyethylenimine polymers which are commercially available. The 1120 is a polyethylenimine product produced specifically for flocculation applications.

TABLE 11.1. Commerically Available Polyethylenimines.

Product	Molecular Weight	Per Cent Active
Polyethylenimine 6	600	99
Polyethylenimine 12	1,200	99
Polyethylenimine 18	1,800	99
Polyethylenimine 600	40– 60,000	33
Polyethylenimine 1000	50–100,000	33
Polyethylenimine 1120	50–100,000	33

Polyethylenimine 600E, an ethoxylated polyethylenimine, is also commercially available. In polyethylenimine 600E the primary and secondary amines are essentially all converted to tertiary amines. The resulting polymer contains approximately equivalent amounts of hydroxyl and tertiary amine groups. This material is supplied as a 40 per cent aqueous solution.

Toxicity

The polyethylenimine polymers are low in acute oral toxicity and are only slightly irritating to the skin, but are moderately irritating to the eyes. In general the polyethylenimine products are less toxic than comparable ethylene amines due to the higher molecular weights obtained in polymerization. However, anhydrous polymers should be handled with care, taking necessary precautions to avoid eye contact since irritation and injury may result. Dilute aqueous solutions of the polymer solutions are not likely to cause more than transient eye irritation, therefore require no special precautions in their handling.

PHYSICAL PROPERTIES

The polyethylenimine polymers are supplied as viscous liquids with their viscosity a function of molecular weight and the concentration of the polymer in solution. The polymers are hygroscopic and amorphous; films cannot be prepared except from modified forms. Analysis indicates that polyethylenimine contains 32.5 per cent nitrogen and the polymer is in reality a polymeric amine displaying basic amine characteristics.

Basicity and Ionic Properties

The polymers react as weak bases in aqueous systems and the pH varies with the degree of polymerization. These polymers are more basic than ammonia. The primary nitrogens are the most basic, then the secondary, and finally the tertiary. This is just the reverse of organic textbook information on amines. This is due to the steric hindrance effect of the polymer.

Because of its cationic nature the polymers are highly substantive to cellulose and display a high affinity for anionic materials such as starch, glass fiber, and other similar materials. The number of charged nitrogens depend on the pH of the solution. At a pH of 10.5 approximately 1 nitrogen in 40 is charged, pH of 7, 1 nitrogen in 10 and at pH of 4, 1 nitrogen in 2 is charged. The cationic nature also plays an important role in paper, waste, and water treatment, and in other flocculation uses.

Solubility

These polymers are soluble in water and in the lower alcohols, and they are generally soluble in all proportions. An exothermic heat of solution is produced when the anhydrous polymers are mixed with water. The temperature increase is proportional to the quantity of polymer added. Table 11.2 describes some of their solubility characteristics.

TABLE 11.2. Solubility of Polyethylenimine.

Solvent	PEI 6	PEI 12	PEI 18	PEI 600	PEI 1000	PEI 1120
Water	∞	∞	∞	∞	∞	∞
Methanol	∞	∞	∞	∞	∞	∞
Ethanol	∞	∞	∞	Yes	Yes	Yes
Isopropanol	∞	∞	∞	Yes	Yes	Yes
Butanol	∼10%	Yes	Yes	No	No	No
Tetrahydrofuran	No	No	No	No	No	No
Toluene	No	No	No	No	No	No

Compatibility

Polyethylenimine polymers are compatible with most of the nonionic materials. These include starch, Methocel®, casein, and many of the natural gums. The polymers are generally incompatible with anionic constituents and are usually precipitated from solution in such systems.

Table 11.3 describes some of the physical properties of the polyethylenimine polymers.

TABLE 11.3. Physical Properties of Polyethylenimine Polymers.

	PEI 6	PEI 12	PEI 18	PEI 600	PEI 1000	PEI 1120
Molecular wt. $\overline{M}n$	600	1200	1800	40–50,000	50–100,000	50–100,000
Assay, wt. % min. (as C_2H_5N)	99	99	99	33	33	33
Density, lb/gal. at 25C	8.60	8.64	8.67	8.79	8.82	8.3
Color, APHA max.	400	400	400	200	200	200
Viscosity, cps, Brookfield at 25C						
As supplied	500–2500	3500–7000	8500–15,000	<5000	15–25,000	15–25,000
5% aqueous solution	2.3	3.1	4.1	28	1200	1200
pH, 5% aqueous solution	10.6	10.6	10.6	10.0	9.8	9.8

Thermal Stability

In many of the processes involving the polyethylenimines heat is used to dry or modify the polymer. Thermogravimetric analyses were conducted in air and nitrogen atmospheres. Figure 1.1 describes the thermal properties of a 33 per cent aqueous solution of polyethylenimine 1000. (Initial weight loss is attributed to water.) Figure 1.2 is a similar curve obtained with polyethylenimine 12, an anhydrous polymer. Since degradation is a function of time as well as temperature, it may be reasoned that prolonged heating at an elevated temperature will cause degradation of the polymer.

It is well established that the polymers possess good thermal stability when compared to other organic polyelectrolytes. As evidenced by Figures 1.1 and 1.2, the decomposition of the polyethylenimines is an endothermic process under a nitrogen atmosphere and is exothermic in air environments. Oxidation is a contributing factor in the degradation of the polymers at high temperatures in air atmospheres.

Chemical Reactivity

The primary, secondary, and tertiary amine nitrogens available in the polyethylenimine polymers provide versatility to the polymer family as chemical intermediates. Virtually any reaction possible with simple amines is possible with polyethylenimines. Through the addition or substitution of various reactive groups a number of polymers with widely diverse properties can be prepared from polyethylenimine. Theoretically, 75 per cent of the nitrogen moieties in the polymer chain have active hydrogens available for reaction. A few of the possible reactions are:

Aldehydes and Ketones

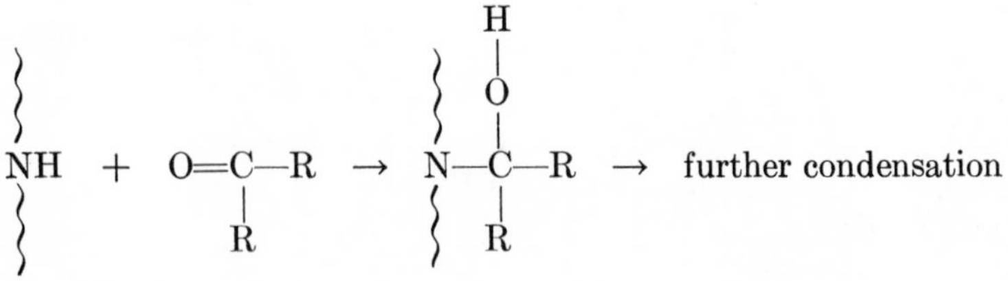

$$
\left\{\ NH\ +\ O{=}C{-}R\ \rightarrow\ N{-}\overset{\overset{\displaystyle H}{|}\ \overset{\displaystyle O}{|}}{C}{-}R\ \rightarrow\ \text{further condensation}
$$

Formaldehyde has been reacted with polyethylenimine to give reactive sites for linking other materials or for cross-linking the polyethylenimine itself.

Alkyl Halides

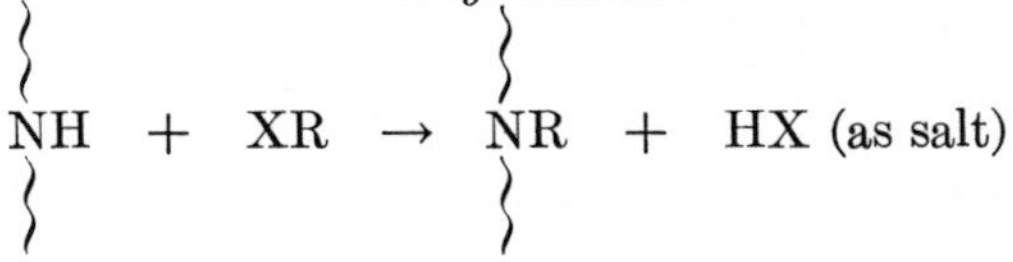

$$
\left\{\ NH\ +\ XR\ \rightarrow\ \left\{\ NR\ +\ HX\ \text{(as salt)}\right.
$$

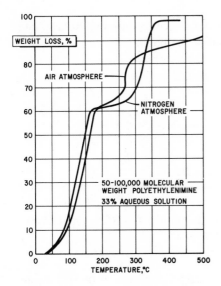

FIGURE 11.1 Thermogravimetric analysis of a 33 per cent aqueous solution of Dow polyethylenimine 1000.

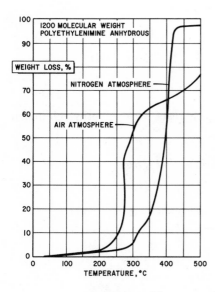

FIGURE 11.2 Thermogravimetric analysis of anhydrous Dow polyethylenimine 12.

Alkyl monohalides are used to make polyethylenimine hydrophobic whereas dihalides are utilized to cross-link the polymer.

Isocyanates and Thioisocyanates

$$\text{NH} + \text{O}{=}\text{C}{=}\text{N}{-}\text{R} \rightarrow \overset{\overset{\displaystyle O}{\|}}{\text{N}{-}\text{C}{-}\text{NHR}}$$

Activated Double Bonds

$$\text{NH} + \overset{R}{\underset{R}{\diagdown}}\text{C}{=}\text{C}\overset{R}{\underset{R}{\diagup}} \rightarrow \text{N}{-}\overset{\overset{R}{|}}{\underset{\underset{R}{|}}{\text{C}}}{-}\overset{\overset{R}{|}}{\underset{\underset{R}{|}}{\text{CH}}} \quad \text{(Where one of the R's is an activating group)}$$

Activated double bonds add readily to the primary and secondary amines of polyethylenimine to give highly useful products. Thus acrylonitrile reacts polyethylenimine in an aqueous solution at room temperature to give a product useful for dye binding applications in paper and textiles.

Epoxides

$$\text{NH} + R_2\text{C}\overset{\overset{\displaystyle O}{\diagup\diagdown}}{-\!-\!-}\text{CR}_2 \rightarrow \text{N}{-}\overset{\overset{R}{|}}{\underset{\underset{R}{|}}{\text{C}}}{-}\overset{\overset{R}{|}}{\underset{\underset{R}{|}}{\text{C}}}{-}\text{OH}$$

Both ethylene oxide and propylene oxide react with polyethylenimine in aqueous solutions.

Cyanamides, Guanidines, and Ureas

$$\text{NH} + \text{H}_2\text{N}{-}\overset{\overset{\displaystyle O}{\|}}{\text{C}}{-}\text{R} \rightarrow \text{N}{-}\overset{\overset{\displaystyle O}{\|}}{\text{C}}{-}\text{R} + \text{NH}_3$$

Acids, Anhydrides and Alkyl Halides

$$\text{NH} + \text{H}{-}\overset{\overset{\displaystyle O}{\|}}{\text{O}}{-}\text{C}{-}\text{R} \rightarrow \left[\overset{\text{H}}{\underset{\text{H}}{\diagup\text{N}\diagdown}}\right]^{+} \overset{\text{O}^{-}}{-}\text{O}{-}\overset{\|}{\text{C}}{-}\text{R} \xrightarrow{\Delta} \text{N}{-}\overset{\overset{\displaystyle O}{\|}}{\text{C}}{-}\text{R} + \text{H}_2\text{O}$$

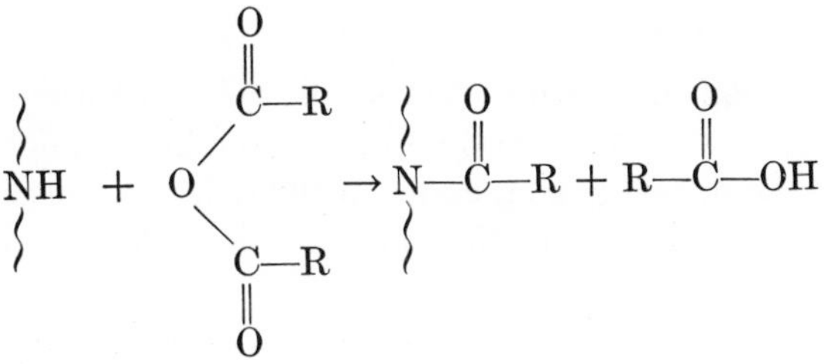

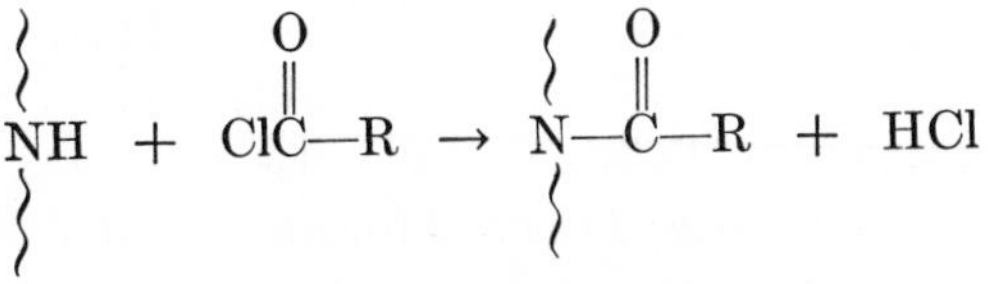

$$
\NH + O
\begin{array}{c}
\overset{O}{\underset{\|}{C}}-R \\
\\
\underset{\|}{C}-R \\
O
\end{array}
\rightarrow \N-\overset{O}{\underset{\|}{C}}-R + R-\overset{O}{\underset{\|}{C}}-OH
$$

$$
\NH + Cl\overset{O}{\underset{\|}{C}}-R \rightarrow \N-\overset{O}{\underset{\|}{C}}-R + HCl
$$

A number of fatty acids may be reacted with polyethylenimine to give products which display both hydrophobic and hydrophilic properties. These products demonstrate performance as detergents and surface active agents. Acylation by either acid anhydrides or acid chlorides may be accomplished in either aqueous or alcohol solution.

APPLICATIONS

Paper

The first commercial use of polyethylenimine was developed as a wet strength additive in the manufacture of paper. The polymers are still used in Europe for this purpose, but U.S. applications are limited in scope.

Another application is based on the polymer's ability to enhance the dewatering rate of pulp in the manufacture of paper and paperboard. The use of polyethylenimine as a "drainage aid" is effective in concentrations as low as 0.05 to 0.5 per cent based on the weight of the dry pulp. The polyethylenimine is best utilized by addition to the pulp system after beating. Addition of the polyethylenimines under proper conditions offers significant increases in machine speeds which result in a more economical process for paper manufacture.

Polyethylenimine, due to its cationic nature, displays a sharp increase in the retention of paper fines, dyes, pigments, fillers, and starch in the papermaking process. The affinity of the cationic polymer for the anionic cellulose pulp is the basis for this increased retention on the "wire" of the paper machine. Needless to say this provides economical advantages to the paper manufacturer by significantly reducing the amount of additives lost in normal processing.

Adhesives and Coatings

Based on its multifunctional properties, polyethylenimine improves aqueous adhesive formulations by providing (a) improved bonding through electrostatic bonds, (b) improved bonding on nonpolar films, (c) improved water resistance, and (d) chemical modification and introduction of new functional groups into the system.

Adhesive applications represent one of the most promising areas for polyethylenimine and the modified polyethylenimine products. The polymers and their reaction products are currently used as adhesives or as additives to adhesive systems which have proven utility in bonding a wide variety of materials. These adhesive systems may be divided into two classes: general adhesives, and tie-coat adhesives which are used to bond together dissimilar substrates.

As general adhesives the polyethylenimines may be used in tire cord adhesives, coatings for fiber glass, coatings for synthetic fibers, etc.

The bonding of dissimilar substrates is best exemplified by the recent development of polyethylene coated paper and similar laminates. Adhesion of polyethylene to paper is basically poor and may be greatly improved by using polyethylenimine. This can be accomplished by applying a very thin film of the adhesive to the paper to which the polyethylene is to be applied. A very light application, generally under 0.05 pounds for 3,000 square feet, is usually sufficient to provide the necessary adhesion for the laminate.

Commercially, polyethylenimine is now used as a primer for milk carton board stock which is subsequently laminated with polyethylene. Any number of plastic films can be laminated to paper in this manner. In addition, polyethylenimine can function as a "tie-coat" for the bonding of one-film substrates to another, polyolefins to metal, and many other combinations involving resins, papers, and plastic coatings.

Flocculation

The large share of suspended organic solids that are found in nature are negatively charged and are readily attracted to and flocculated by polyethylenimine. The high molecular weight polyethylenimines are especially suited as flocculants. They are used in waste and water purification and in clarification of many process effluents. The clarification of plant recycle water is important in many operations and the use of polyethylenimine as settling aids significantly improves the efficiency of such operations.

Textiles

The high substantivity of the polyethylenimine polymers to cellulose is important when used to modify cotton fabrics. The polymers are also substantive to synthetic fabrics but to a lesser degree. The polymers have been used to improve dyeability and color fastness in fabrics, and to enhance adhesion of water-proofing and flame-proofing finishes to the fabric.

The advantages offered by modified polyethylenimines are illustrated by its use in viscose production; by cyanoethylating the polymer, and then adding the derivative to the viscose spinning bath, the polymer becomes an integral part of the rayon fiber, and contributes improved dyeability and color fastness to the finished product. Quaternized polyethylenimine can be used to improve antistatic properties of fabric, and improve dyeability in textile printing applications. Epoxy-modified polyethylenimines can be used to produce shrink-proof and water-proof textiles.

Ion Exchange Resins

The polyethylenimines have been used to prepare complexes of copper and other heavy metals, which are useful in ion exchange materials. The polyethylenimine-based ion exchange resins can be greatly improved by the use of various cross-linking agents such as ethylene dibromide and epichlorohydrin. The resulting materials are effective ion exchangers, and may be formed as ion exchange membranes under proper conditions.

Photography

Polyethylenimine has been cited in many literature references for possible use in photographic areas. Polyethylenimine has been used to control the grain growth of halide salts. The polymers can be used as extenders for gelatin and gelatin substitutes can be prepared by cross-linking with diketene.

Mining

Polyethylenimine and various derivatives find use as flotation agents, for the removal of silica or sand from minerals such as iron. The flotation agents may be prepared by reacting the polymer with a fatty acid or tall oil, to produce the corresponding amide. The resulting product is hydrophobic and functions by adhering to silica particles through its cationic sites while the lipophilic portion serves to carry the particle to the surface.

Plastics

The use of polyethylenimine is effective in preventing static buildup on plastic components and on plastic films and containers. Its effect as an antistat is due to its conductivity, thereby "discharging" the plastic surface.

Petroleum

Modified polyethylenimines find use as additives to motor oils and gasoline. These additives function as detergents, pour point depressants, suspending agents, stabilizers, and anti-corrosion additives.

The polyethylenimine derivatives also find utility in the oil field itself. Many agents used in the manufacture of petroleum products are based on polyethylenimine demulsifiers and anti-corrosion agents.

Modification of polyethylenimine with carboxylic acids provides useful emulsifiers in asphalt processing. The resulting asphalt products display improved adhesion to aggregate used in road construction, and permit the use of wet aggregates, and provide improved road life.

Rubber

The lower molecular weight polyethylenimines display utility as coagulation aids for styrene-butadiene rubber latexes. These polymers function effectively in hot, cold, oil-extended, and master-batch latex systems. They are used to control "crumb" size and reduce latex fines, thus improving yield and alleviating disposal problems.

The polyethylenimine polymers also improve the adhesion of rubber to various substrates such as cotton, rayon, polyester, and glass fibers.

Agriculture

Aqueous polyethylenimine has been used as a soil conditioner. Crosslinked polyethylenimine is an effective erosion control agent useful in controlling soil damage caused by water "run-off."

Curing Agent for Epoxy Resins

The anhydrous polyethylenimine polymers are especially suited as curing agents for epoxy resins. They can be used as "all purpose" curing agents in many commercial epoxy resins systems used as laminating adhesives and castings.

The polyethylenimine polymers display several advantages over many of the ethylene amines in epoxy systems such as improved tensile strength, higher heat distortion temperature, and lower exothermic heat during curing.

Index

Dat

JUL 1 8 1968